CROWN
Do Well

Discovering God's Way
Of Handling
MONEY

A FINANCIAL STUDY FOR TEENS
By Howard and Bev Dayton

STUDENT MANUAL

In the future . . .

When you become an adult, we hope that you will enroll in the Crown small group study. This will help you with the issues you will face at that stage of your life.

Should you or your parents wish to learn more, please visit our Web site at Crown.org and listen to Crown programs on your local Christian radio station.

ISBN 978-1-56427-033-7

January 2012 Edition

Schedule

Chapter	Subject	Put It into Practice!
1	Introduction	None This Week
2	God's Part & Our Part	Recording Income & Spending / Deed
3	Debt	Recording Income & Spending / Money-Saving Ideas
4	Counsel	Your Checking Account / Recording Income & Spending
5	Honesty	Recording Income & Spending / Estimating Your Budget
6	Giving	Beginning Your Budget
7	Work	Job Resume
8	Saving	Your Savings Account
9	Friends	Your Financial Goals
10	Go For It!	Insurance Needs / Your Financial Statement

Welcome!

We're Glad You're Here!

You've taken the first step toward gaining financial freedom. It's our hope that you will gain wisdom and use that wisdom not only to change your life, but to be leaders in your home, school, and even in your community. Sound like a big job? It is, but with this exciting study you will learn how to apply some of the greatest financial principles in the world, principles that come from the Bible.

So Get Ready!

You're about to begin an incredible adventure, and by the time you're finished, you'll have a solid grasp on how to handle money. Who knows, you may even become the person others come to for help!

It's Up to You!

No study, no matter how great it is, will work by itself. You have to be willing to put in effort to make it work for you. We all know how tough it is to keep up with commitments, even when you've said you will. So Crown has some requirements and one Golden Rule for this study. The Golden Rule is designed to help you be faithful.

Here it is:

The Golden Rule

Anyone who doesn't complete the requirements for a chapter will not be allowed to participate in that session's discussion.

(In other words, *you can't talk!*)

Now, keeping that rule in mind, here are the requirements:

Memorize It!

It was important when you were a kid; it's even more important now. The only way to get these biblical principles firmly rooted in your mind is to memorize them. There is an assigned verse for each chapter.

Check It Out!

Each chapter has questions and information you'll need to jump-start your thinking. Each person is expected to complete the questions before the meeting. That way you'll know ahead of time exactly what you think about the topic, and you'll be ready to discuss it.

Put It into Practice!

These are practical exercises to help you put what you've learned to use.

Prayer Log!

If you're taking this study in a small group, everyone should pray for each other. If your group is large, divide into smaller groups so you can take prayer requests and pray daily for those in your smaller group. It may seem like a hassle at first, but give it time. You'll be amazed at how exciting it will become when you can look back at all God has done through your prayers.

Introduction

"Therefore if you have not been faithful in the use of worldly* wealth, who will entrust the true riches to you?" (Luke 16:11)

* The word "worldly" from the NIV has been substituted for "unrighteous" in the NASB to clarify the meaning.

God's Part & Our Part

"Everything in the heavens and earth is yours, O Lord, and this is your kingdom. We adore you as being in control of everything. Riches and honor come from you alone, and you are the Ruler of all mankind; your hand controls power and might, and it is at your discretion that men are made great and given strength" (1 Chronicles 29:11-12, TLB).

Debt

"Just as the rich rule the poor, so the borrower is servant to the lender" (Proverbs 22:7, TLB).

Counsel

"The way of a fool is right in his own eyes, but a wise man is he who listens to counsel" (Proverbs 12:15).

Honesty

"You shall not steal, nor deal falsely, nor lie to one another" (Leviticus 19:11).

Giving

"Remember the words of the Lord Jesus, that He Himself said, 'It is more blessed to give than to receive'" (Acts 20:35).

Work

"Whatever you do, do your work heartily, as for the Lord rather than for men.... It is the Lord Christ whom you serve" (Colossians 3:23-24).

Saving

"The wise man saves for the future, but the foolish man spends whatever he gets" (Proverbs 21:20, TLB).

Friends

"Let no one look down on your youthfulness, but rather in speech, conduct, love, faith and purity, show yourself an example of those who believe" (1 Timothy 4:12).

Go for It!

"I have learned to be content in whatever circumstances I am. I know how to get along with humble means, and I also know how to live in prosperity.... I can do all things through Him who strengthens me" (Philippians 4:11-13).

Chapter 1

Introduction

Chapter 1 Introduction

Memorize It!

"Therefore if you have not been faithful in the use of worldly* wealth, who will entrust the true riches to you?"
(Luke 16:11)

* The word "worldly" from the NIV has been substituted for "unrighteous" in the NASB to clarify the meaning.

Check It Out!

1.) Read Isaiah 55:8-9.

Based on this passage, do you think God's principles of handling money are different from the way most people handle money?

What do you think would be the greatest difference(s)?

2.) How do the following influence the way you spend?

Comparing your spending with that of friends —

Watching TV programs and commercials —

The Internet —

Studying the Bible —

Should your relationship with Christ influence the way you spend money? If so, how?

Do you think the Lord wants you to change the way you spend money? If so, what are some of the things you believe need changing?

3.) Read Luke 16:11.

What does this verse say about handling money and receiving true riches?

What do you think are the "true riches" referred to in this verse?

4.) Read the Introductory Notes on pages 12-13.

What information especially interested you?

Why do you think the Bible says so much about money?

Introduction

Notes

Would it surprise you . . .

to learn that the Bible says a lot about money? From beginning to end, Genesis to Revelation, there are more than 2,350 verses on how to handle money!

Sixteen of the 38 parables in the Gospels deal with handling money and possessions. In Matthew, Mark, Luke, and John alone, one out of 10 verses (288 total!) addresses money. Jesus talked more about money than about almost anything else.

So what's the big deal? Why did Jesus spend so much time talking about money? There are two simple reasons.

Reason #1: Your Relationship with God

Check out Luke 16:11. Jesus makes some pretty amazing statements regarding the ways we handle money. He says, *"Therefore if you have not been faithful in the use of worldly* wealth, who will entrust the true riches to you?"* What are the true riches? A strong relationship with Jesus. So, this makes it clear that how we handle our money impacts our relationship with Christ. If we follow the principles in the Scriptures, we will grow closer to God. Guaranteed. However, if we ignore those principles and handle money carelessly, our relationship with Him will suffer. Also guaranteed.

In the parable of the talents, three servants were given money to use while their master was away. Only two servants used the money wisely and were able to give the master even more money than they had been given in the first place! Obviously, the master was thrilled. He congratulated the servants, telling them, *"Well done, good and faithful slave. You were faithful with a few things, I will put you in charge of many things; enter into the joy of your master"* (Matthew 25:21).

Put quite simply, the Bible is your instruction manual for wise money management. Think about it. Suppose you go out and buy a PlayStation or Xbox. What's the first thing you do when you get home? Put it together of course! And how do you do that? By tossing the instructions and guessing which wire goes where? Yeah, right. Not unless you're some kind of electronics guru. But if you're like most of us, the last thing you want is to end up with a mess of wires and blinking

> The **Bible** is your Instruction Manual for wise **money management**.

digital displays. No, you pull out the instruction booklet, read it, and follow what it says.

The same goes for the Bible and money. When you use the Bible as your Instruction Manual, you learn to handle money properly and, like the servant, you have the opportunity to "enter into the joy" of a closer relationship with the Lord.

Reason #2: Practical Help

God realizes that money will be a huge part of our lives. And, because God cares for us, He wants to help us handle money wisely. Therefore, the Lord gave us some very practical truths in the Bible that are like a map to guide us on our financial journey. They are a gift from a loving God intended to help us.

In this book you'll learn what God wants you to know about:

- how to earn money in your job
- how to save regularly
- how to give generously
- how to spend wisely
- how to stay out of debt
- and much, much more!

Take the Challenge!

A close friend challenged me to join him in a study of Scripture to find out what the Lord said about handling money. Believe it or not, we read the entire Bible! We discovered 2,350 verses dealing with money. Not only were we surprised at how practical the Word of God is about money, but we discovered a secret—something that helped us put money into perspective. And it's simple: The responsibility for handling money is split in two. One part is ours, the other is God's! God knew how tough this

would be for us, and He knew we couldn't handle it on our own. Rather than leave the whole burden on our shoulders, He kept certain responsibilities and gave others to us.

When my friend and I realized this, we were really excited. We had found that most of the frustration in handling money is because we do not realize which responsibilities are ours and which are the Lord's.

So get ready. You're about to discover some incredible truths that will help you for the rest of your life!

Chapter 2
God's Part & Our Part

Chapter

God's Part & Our Part

Memorize It!

"Everything in the heavens and earth is yours, O Lord, and this is your kingdom. We adore you as being in control of everything. Riches and honor come from you alone, and you are the Ruler of all mankind; your hand controls power and might, and it is at your discretion that men are made great and given strength" (1 Chronicles 29:11-12, TLB).

Put It into Practice!

- Read the material on pages 26-28.
- Begin recording your income and spending (see page 29).
- Complete the "Deed" on page 31.

Check It Out!

1.) Read Deuteronomy 10:14 and 1 Corinthians 10:26.

What do these verses have to say about your possessions and who owns them?

Read the following verses. What do they say God owns?

Leviticus 25:23

Psalm 50:10-12

Haggai 2:8

How often do you recognize the true owner of your possessions? Share two practical suggestions that will help you recognize God's ownership of your things.

1.)

2.)

2.) Read 1 Chronicles 29:11-12.

What do these verses say about the Lord's ability to control circumstances?

Do you normally recognize the Lord's control in your life? In the lives of others? If not, how can you become more consistent in recognizing His control?

3.) Read Genesis 45:4-8 and Romans 8:28.

Why is it important to realize that God controls and uses even the difficult times in your life?

Describe a difficult time you have experienced. How did the Lord use it for good in your life?

Read Psalm 34:9-10 and Matthew 6:31-33. What has the Lord promised about meeting your needs?

How does this apply to you today?

4.) Read 1 Corinthians 4:2.

According to this verse, what are you required to do as a steward?

How would you define a steward?

Read Luke 16:10. Describe the principle found in this verse.

How does this apply in your situation?

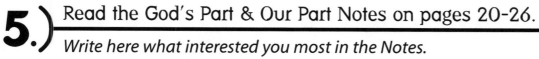

5.) Read the God's Part & Our Part Notes on pages 20-26.

Write here what interested you most in the Notes.

How will you apply what you have learned?

What benefits do you think you will experience when you do these things?

*Please write your prayer requests in your **Prayer Log** before coming to class.*

God's Part & Our Part

Notes

Most people don't think . . .

that God has anything to do with their money. Are they ever wrong! Let's look at the responsibilities God has with our money.

God Is the Owner

The Lord owns all our stuff. *"The earth is the Lord's, and all that it contains"* (Psalm 24:1).

When you checked out the Scriptures in the Look It Up! section you discovered they list some of the things that God owns. Leviticus 25:23 identifies Him as the owner of all the land: *"The land is Mine."* Haggai 2:8 says, *"'The silver is Mine, and the gold is Mine,' declares the Lord of hosts."* And Psalm 50:10-12 tells us: *"Every beast of the forest is Mine, the cattle on a thousand hills ... everything that moves in the field is Mine. If I were hungry, I would not tell you, for the world is Mine, and all it contains."*

The Lord is the Creator of all things, and He has never given the ownership of His creation to us. He created the earth for us to use and care for. But He never handed us the keys and said, "OK, kids, it's all yours."

When we recognize God's ownership, every spending decision becomes a spiritual decision. No longer do we ask, "Lord, what do you want me to do with **my** money?" Instead we say,

"GOD, YOU HAVE A DENT IN YOUR CAR!"

"Lord, what do you want me to do with **Your** money?"

What's more, recognizing the Lord's ownership will bring you a great sense of peace and contentment. Shortly after Jason came to grips with God's ownership, he purchased a new car. He had driven the car for only two days when someone plowed into the side of it. Now, I don't know about you, but if someone wrecked my brand new car, I might be tempted to freak out! But Jason reacted quite differently! He simply said, "Lord, I don't know why You want a dent in Your car, but now You've got a big one!" Now that's contentment!

Consistently recognizing God's ownership is difficult. Many people believe God owns all they have but still live as if this were not true.

To help you remember God's ownership: Every day for the next 30 days, as soon as you wake up and just before you go to sleep, meditate on 1 Chronicles 29:11-12. Make it a special prayer every day to ask the Lord to make you aware of His ownership.

God Is in Control

God is ultimately in control of every event that occurs. The Bible is full of verses that prove this, including 1 Chronicles 29:11, *"We adore you as being in control of everything"* (TLB) and Psalm 135:6, *"Whatever the Lord pleases, He does, in heaven and in earth."*

The Lord is in control even of difficult events. *"I am the Lord, and there is no other, the One forming light and creating darkness, causing well-being and creating calamity"* (Isaiah 45:6-7).

Hard to believe, isn't it, that God is in control of even tough times in our lives? But He is. He takes every situation and uses it to teach us and to bring His good into our lives. Romans 8:28 says, *"We know that God causes all things to work together for good to those who love God, to those who are called according to His purpose."* We don't always understand why the Lord allows difficult times, but there are at least two possible reasons:

1. To Accomplish His Intentions

As a teen, Joseph was sold into slavery by his jealous brothers. Joseph eventually understood that the Lord had sent him to Egypt to save his family during a terrible famine. When he finally saw his brothers again, he wasn't angry or vengeful. Instead he told them: *"Do not be grieved or angry with yourselves, because you sold me here, for God sent me before you to preserve life ... it was not you who sent me here, but God"* (Genesis 45:5, 8).

How about you? How would you feel if your family did something like this to you? Could you trust God and believe in His control?

2. To Discipline Us

The Bible says it best: *"Those whom the Lord loves He disciplines. ... He disciplines us for our good, so that we may share His holiness. All discipline for the moment seems not to be joyful, but sorrowful; yet to those who have been trained by it, afterwards it yields the peaceful fruit of righteousness"* (Hebrews 12:6, 10-11). When we are disobedient, we can expect our loving Father to discipline us, often through difficult times, in an effort to turn us from our sin.

God Is Our Provider

Ever come home, after a loooooong road-trip with your family, ready for your favorite snack? You make a beeline for the fridge, pull it open, and find ... the electricity went out while you were away, and all your food is spoiled!

It's an awful feeling to have a need and feel as though it's not going to be met. Well, that won't happen with God. He has promised to provide for our needs. *"Seek first His kingdom and His righteousness, and all these things* [food and clothing] *will be added to you"* (Matthew 6:33).

This isn't some God who doesn't know what He's talking about! He fed manna to the children of Israel in the wilderness. And He fed 5,000 people with five little loaves of bread and two fish! He told Elijah, *"I have commanded the ravens to provide for you. ... The ravens brought him bread and meat in the morning and bread and meat in the evening"* (1 Kings 17:4, 6).

This same God, a God of miracles and relia-

> This same **God**, a God of miracles and reliability, has promised to provide for **our needs**.

bility, has promised to provide for our needs.

It's odd, but God is both predictable and unpredictable. He is totally predictable in His faithfulness in taking care of us; what we cannot predict is how the Lord will provide. He uses various ways, some of them quite amazing: a raise in your hourly wages at Burger Barn, a gift from Aunt Sally, a sale at your favorite store, or an expected baby-sitting job. However He provides for us, you can count on this: God is faithful.

Because God provides for us, we can live in peace and contentment. (Notice a pattern here?) In 1 Timothy 6:8, we read, *"If we have food and covering, with these we shall be content."*

As World War II was drawing to a close, the Allied armies gathered up many orphans. They were placed in camps where they were well fed; and yet, they were filled with fear and slept poorly. Finally, someone came up with a solution. Each child was given a piece of bread to hold after he went to bed.

This bread was not to eat. If a child was hungry, he or she would be given more. But this particular piece of bread was just to hold. Amazingly enough, the children's fear disappeared. They went to bed knowing that they would have food to eat the next day, and that simple guarantee gave them the peace and contentment they needed to sleep.

Similarly, the Lord has given us His guarantee. Our "piece of bread" is His promises to us in the Bible. *"My God shall supply all your needs according to His riches,"* we are told in Philippians 4:19. And with that promise tucked in our hearts, we can be content and at peace.

> Because God provides for us, we can live in peace and **contentment**.

God Wants Us to Know Him

Ever been lost in a strange place and asked someone for directions? Even if that person sounds like he knows what he's talking about, you're not positive that his directions will get you where you want to go. Ever wonder why that is? Probably because you don't know him! Now, think about being lost and seeing someone you know who has lived in that area for 15 years! Think you'd feel more confident about his directions? It's far easier to trust someone you know, someone who has shown you they are dependable.

God knows it's easier to trust someone you know. That's why He invites us to get to know Him. He wants us to learn everything we can about Him. Do you know who God is? Who He really is? He is all-powerful, all-wise, all-knowing. He created everything that exists. Everything! He *"stretched out the heavens and laid the foundations of the earth"* (Isaiah 51:13). Too often we try to shrink God down and limit Him to human abilities. So how can we understand who God really is? Simple! Study what the Bible says about Him. Here are just a few of the things the Bible reveals about God.

He Is Lord of the Universe

Take a look at some of God's names and characteristics: Creator, Almighty, Eternal, Lord of lords, and King of kings.

The Lord's power goes far beyond our understanding. Astronomers estimate there are more than 100 billion galaxies in the universe, each containing billions of stars. The distance from one end of a galaxy to the other is often measured in millions of light years. Though our sun is a relatively small star, it could contain over one million planets the size of the earth, and, at its center, it has a temperature of 20 million degrees. Isaiah knew God was awesome. He said in Isaiah 40:26, *"Lift up your eyes on high and see who has created these stars, the One who leads forth their host by number, He calls them all by name; because of the greatness of His might and the strength of His power, not one of them is missing."*

He Is Lord of the Nations

Study how the Lord rules nations and people. Isaiah 40:21-24 tells us, *"Do you not know? Have you not heard? . . . It is He who sits above the circle of the earth, and its inhabitants are like grasshoppers. . . . He it is who reduces rulers to nothing, who makes the judges of the earth meaningless. Scarcely have they been planted, scarcely have they been sown, scarcely has their stock taken root in the earth, but He merely blows on them, and they wither."*

Acts 17:26 says, *"He [the Lord] . . . scattered the nations across the face of the earth. He decided beforehand which should rise and fall, and when. He determined their boundaries"* (TLB).

He Is Lord of the Individual

God is not some "force." He is involved with each of us as individuals. Psalm 139:3-4,16 says, *"You are familiar with all my ways. Before a word is on my tongue you know it completely, O Lord. . . . All the days ordained for me were written in your book before one of them came to be"* (NIV). The Lord is so involved in our lives that He tells us, *"The very hairs of your head are all numbered"* (Matthew 10:30). Our heavenly Father knows us the best and loves us the most.

God hung the stars in space, made the earth's towering mountains and mighty oceans, and determined the future of nations. Jeremiah observed: *"Nothing is too difficult for You"* (Jeremiah 32:17). Yet He knows when a sparrow falls to the ground. So you can be sure He knows and cares about everything that happens to you, too.

What's a Steward?

Okay. We've spent some time checking out what God's part is in managing money. Now let's take a look at our part. The word that best describes our part is "steward." You've probably heard the word before, but do you know what it means? It means you are a manager.

God is the owner of everything you have. But He has given you an assignment: to be a steward—a manager. He asks you to take care of some of His possessions. So what exactly does that mean? Do you have to be perfect? And should you be shaking in your boots if you mess up? Not at all. God will give you the wisdom you need to do your part right. The only thing you are required to do is be faithful.

This is clearly shown in 1 Corinthians 4:2: *"It is required of stewards that a person be found trustworthy."* The first step is simple: Know what you are required to do. Imagine starting a new job. It's your first day and you're ready to find out what you are supposed to do. But instead of giving you any instructions, your new boss just tells you, "Welcome! Now get out there and get busy." Think you'll do a good job? Probably not!

God knows you need guidelines to do a good job as a steward, and He doesn't leave you hanging. He's given you a detailed instruction manual—the Bible. And when it comes to faithfulness as a steward, the Bible gives two important guidelines.

Guideline #1: Be Faithful No Matter How Much—or How Little—You Have

Take a look at Matthew 25:14-30, the parable of the talents. *"It is just like a man about to go on a journey, who called his own slaves and entrusted his possessions to them. To one he gave five talents, to another, two, and to another, one"* (Matthew 25:14-15).

This "boss" was going to be gone for a while, and he needed someone to watch over his things. When he returned, he held each one accountable for managing the possessions he'd been given. Check out the master's approval of the faithful servant who received the five talents: *"Well done, good and faithful servant; you were faithful with a few things, I will put you in charge of many things; enter into the joy of your master"* (Matthew 25:21). The one who had been given two talents received the same reward as the servant who had been given the five talents (see Matthew 25:23). It wasn't the amount that mattered, but what the steward did with what he was given.

The Lord requires faithfulness in any amount. It doesn't matter how much you have, God wants you to be faithful. As someone once said, "It's not what I would do if a million dollars were my lot; it's what I'm doing with the 10 dollars I've got." So the first part of being a good steward is being faithful with whatever amount you have.

Guideline #2: Be Faithful with All That You Have

Many of us have heard that Christians are to give 10 percent of their income to the Lord. But being a steward doesn't end there. You need to be faithful with 100 percent of what God gives you.

Too many think God only cares about the 10 percent and they are free to do what they want with the rest. This causes them to make unwise financial decisions. Hosea 4:6 reads, *"My people are destroyed for lack of knowledge."* Not knowing what the Bible says about handling money can cause financial problems.

To Whom Are You Responsible?

God knows what you think. In fact, He knows everything about you. Hebrews 4:13 reads, *"Nothing in all creation is hidden from God's sight. Everything is uncovered and laid bare before the eyes of him to whom we must give account"* (NIV).

There is nothing you will ever do or think that the Lord does not know. Think about that for a moment! Second Corinthians 5:9-10 reads, *"So we make it our goal to please him.... For we must all appear before the judgment seat of Christ, that each one may receive what is due him for the things done while in the body, whether good or bad"* (NIV).

One day you are going to stand in front of the Lord and be held accountable for how you managed your money. And because the Lord loves you so much, He wants the best for you here on earth and in heaven. Now that's motivation!

Why Be Responsible?

When you learn to be a faithful steward, you will discover some awesome benefits.

Benefit #1: Closer to the Lord

Remember what the master said to the servant who had been faithful: *"Enter into the joy of your master"* (Matthew 25:21). What is that joy? A closer fellowship with the Lord. As you are faithful, you will grow closer to Christ, and the joy you experience will increase.

Someone once told me that the Lord often allows a person to teach a subject because that person needs to learn more about it than anyone else! That was true for me in the area of money. When I began to apply these principles, I experienced a wonderful improvement in my fellowship with the Lord. Each of the principles is intended to draw us closer to Christ.

Benefit #2: Finances That Are in Order

Two brothers received the same amount of money each week as an allowance. The first brother spent all of his money as soon as he got it on whatever caught his attention. The second brother first gave to the Lord, then put some of his money into a savings account. Guess which brother was able to buy a car first? And guess which brother was always coming to ask the other for a loan?

When you apply God's principles, you will find that dealing with money becomes a joy, not a hassle. You will stay out of debt, spend more wisely, start saving for your future goals, and give even more to the work of Christ.

Three Important Principles of Faithfulness

As you learn to become a faithful steward, it will help you to keep three things in mind.

1.) Waste Not or You Get Fired!

"There was a rich man who had a manager [steward], and this manager was reported to him as squandering his possessions. And he called him and said to him … 'You can no longer be manager [steward]'" (Luke 16:1-2). Being a faithful steward can bring wonderful benefits. However, unfaithfulness can cost you everything.

God has entrusted you with certain things. If you waste them, God may remove you from your position as steward.

A businessman earned a fortune in just three years and then spent it wildly. Today this man is almost bankrupt. He had more than enough money to last him his entire life, but he wasted it foolishly. If you waste what God has given you, you may not be given more.

2.) Be Faithful in Little Things

"He who is faithful in a very little thing is faithful also in much; and he who is unrighteous in a very little thing is unrighteous also in much" (Luke 16:10).

How do you know if a fellow teen is going to take good care of his first car? See how he cared for his bike. How do you know if a salesperson will do a good job serving a big customer? Watch how she served a small customer. If we have the character to be faithful with small things, the Lord knows He can trust us with greater responsibilities.

Someone said, "Small things are small things, but how we handle small things is a big thing."

3.) Be Faithful with Others' Possessions

"If you have not been faithful in the use of that which is another's, who will give you that which is your own?" (Luke 16:12).

A young girl borrowed her sister's bike to go to the library. On the way, she ran it into the curb, bending the wheel. When she returned the damaged bike to her sister, she told her,

"Can you hurry up and get this fixed? I need to go to the library again tomorrow."

Would you be likely to loan your bike to someone who had done this? Not very. It's important that you treat others' possessions with as much care as you treat your own. When someone allows you to use something, are you careful to return it in good condition? Some people have not been given more because they have been unfaithful with others' possessions.

is that they don't understand God's part and our part. But this doesn't have to happen to you. Recognize that God is the Owner of all you have, then become a faithful steward. The rest of the book will help you learn exactly what faithful stewards should be doing with their money. As you apply these principles, you will put yourself in a position to experience God's blessing instead of feeling frustrated.

Summary

Many people are frustrated with their finances. The biggest reason for their frustration

Put It into Practice!

Recording Your Income & Spending / The Deed

As we explained earlier, each chapter contains a helpful exercise called **Put It into Practice!** There will be an explanation, a sample, and a blank sheet for you to use.

One of our goals is to help you to use a simple budget. Many people turn a little green when you mention using a budget. They're afraid a budget will lock them into a rigid system, costing them their freedom and hours of mind-bending calculator punching. But that's not true. As hard as it may be to believe, a budget can be a friend.

Using a budget will be the first step to getting your finances under control. A budget will help to accomplish the things that are important to you.

The first step in setting up a budget is easy: Start recording your income and spending.

Recording Your Income & Spending

It may seem like a pain to record things on paper, but it is still the best way to see what you are actually earning and spending. You have to know this before you start your budget. Trying to put a budget together without this information would be like putting a puzzle together without half the pieces—it will have a lot of holes! Don't try to operate on guesswork. You'll just be wasting your time.

Choose a time every day to enter whatever income you received or whatever you spent on the "Recording Your Income & Spending" worksheet. As you can see, the worksheet is designed with three columns.

1.) **Description.** This allows you to separate your spending into categories.

2.) **Amounts.** Enter the amount that was earned or spent each day.

3.) **Totals for week.** At the end of the week, total the amount in each category and record them here.

Study the sample on the next page. Then use the blank worksheets in each of the next four chapters to record your income and spending.

The Deed

To help you understand God's ownership of your possessions, you are going to transfer them to Him. When property is transferred, a deed often is used. So in this exercise, you will create a deed transferring your possessions to the Lord.

This deed is not legally binding. It's only for your use. By completing this deed (page 31), you establish a time when you acknowledge God's ownership.

OK? Let's get started.

1.) Write today's date at the top of the deed. Then print your name in the space after "from," because you are transfer-ring ownership of your possessions.

2.) Take a look at the sentence, "I transfer to the Lord the ownership of the following possessions." Pray about those possessions you wish to acknowledge that God owns and write them in the space.

3.) Sign your name on the line under the heading "Steward." In the lower left-hand corner there are two blank lines for the signatures of witnesses. Have two others witness your signature to help you accountable acknowledge God as owner of your possessions.

Recording Your Income & Spending

Description	Amounts	Totals for First Week
Income	2.00 + 1.50 + 7.00 + 3.00	13.50
Giving	1.50 + 1.00	2.50
Savings	2.00	2.00
Food	1.25 + .75 + 1.00	3.00
School/Lessons	0	0
Clothing	0	0
Grooming	2.50	2.50
Transportation	.50	.50
Sports	0	0
Entertainment	3.00	3.00
Gifts	0	0
Other:	0	0
Other:	0	0

Recording Your Income & Spending

Description	Amounts	Totals for First Week
Income		
Giving		
Savings		
Food		
School/Lessons		
Clothing		
Grooming		
Transportation		
Sports		
Entertainment		
Gifts		
Other:		
Other:		

Deed

This Deed, Made the ___21st___ day of ___January, 2004___

FROM: ___David___

TO: The Lord

I hereby transfer to the Lord the ownership of the following possessions:

Stereo	Savings Account
Clothes	School Supplies
Surfboard	Fido the Dog
Bike	Stamp Collection
Baseball Equipment	Watch
Computer	

Witnesses who will help me remember the Lord's ownership:

___Mary___

___Peter___

Steward of the possessions above:

___David___

Deed

This Deed, Made the _____ day of _____

FROM: _____

TO: **The Lord**

I hereby transfer to the Lord the ownership of the following possessions:

Witnesses who will help me remember
the Lord's ownership:

Steward of the possessions above:

_____

_____

_____

Chapter 3

Debt

Chapter 3 — Debt

Memorize It!

"Just as the rich rule the poor, so the borrower is servant to the lender" (Proverbs 22:7, TLB).

Put It into Practice!

- Complete the "Money-Saving Ideas" on pages 42-43.
- Continue recording your income and spending on the worksheet on page 37.

Check It Out!

1.) Read Deuteronomy 28:1-2, 12, 15, 43-45.

According to these passages, how was debt viewed in the Old Testament?

What was the cause of someone getting in debt (becoming a borrower) or getting out of debt (becoming a lender)?

Read Proverbs 22:7 and Romans 13:8. What does each of these Scriptures say about debt?

Proverbs 22:7	

Romans 13:8	

2.) Read Psalm 37:21 and Proverbs 3:27-28.

What do these verses say about paying debts?

Psalm 37:21

Proverbs 3:27-28

How will you apply what these verses say in your own life?

3.) How would you define cosigning?

Read Proverbs 17:18 and Proverbs 22:26-27. What does the Bible say about cosigning (some Bible translations refer to this as "striking hands" or "surety")?

Proverbs 17:18

Proverbs 22:26-27

4.) Read the Debt Notes on pages 38-41.

Are you in debt? If so, what steps do you feel the Lord wants you to take to become free of debt?

What did you learn about debt that proved to be especially interesting?

*Please write your prayer requests in your **Prayer Log** before coming to class.*

Recording Your Income & Spending

Description	Amounts	Totals for Second Week
Income		
Giving		
Savings		
Food		
School/Lessons		
Clothing		
Grooming		
Transportation		
Sports		
Entertainment		
Gifts		
Other:		
Other:		

Debt

Notes

Tamika was crying . . .

as she said, "When I first bought my car, I really liked it. It was shiny and new and great to drive. The man who sold it to me said there would only be four years of low, easy payments.

"I believed him. That was my first mistake! There was nothing easy about those payments. All I seemed to do was work to pay for the car. I didn't have time or money to do anything else. I want to sell the car now and be free of debt, but there's one problem: It's not worth what I owe on it. So I can't even sell it, because I would still end up owing money to the bank on the loan."

Many people are drowning in a sea of debt. In a recent year more than 1,500,000 people filed bankruptcy. A survey found that 56 percent of divorces are because of money problems.

How do these problems get started? Don't people realize they can't spend more money than they make? No. Not really. Especially when they see advertisements that tell them to buy now and pay later with "easy" monthly payments. Buying things on credit, going into debt, is easy. But what no one seems to say is that paying the debt is hard, real hard.

What Is Debt?

Debt includes money borrowed from credit card companies, banks, relatives, and so on. It is the money people borrow to buy homes, cars, education, clothes . . . and the list goes on and on and on and . . . well, you get the picture.

What Does Debt Really Cost?

I'm going to tell you a secret, and I want you to remember it for the rest of your life: Debt is expensive! It'll cost you more than you can ever dream. To understand the real cost, let's look at a common type of debt: credit card debt.

Credit Card Debt

Everyone seems to have credit cards today, and millions of people think they are harmless. Can they really be all that dangerous?

You bet. And here's why. Let's say you have $5,560 in credit-card debt at an 18 percent interest rate. The credit card company is nice enough to let you make

"MY CREDIT CARDS ARE ALMOST PAID OFF!"

1. Amount of interest you paid:				
Year 5	Year 10	Year 20	Year 30	Year 40
$5,000	$10,000	$20,000	$30,000	$40,000

2. What you would earn on the $1,000 invested at 12 percent:				
Year 5	Year 10	Year 20	Year 30	Year 40
$6,353	$17,549	$72,052	$241,333	$767,091

3. How much the lender earns from your payment at 18 percent:				
Year 5	Year 10	Year 20	Year 30	Year 40
$7,154	$23,521	$146,628	$790,948	$4,163,213

small payments of only $90 a month. Good deal, right? Wrong. At $90 a month, it will take you more than 30 years to pay back this one loan! But the story doesn't end there. Not by a long shot. You're paying interest, remember? Guess how much you are paying every year to borrow this money from the credit card company? About $1,000! That's roughly $84 a month that you are paying in interest! Take a look at the chart above.

You can see what lenders have known for a long time: Interest can either work for or against you. If you're the lender, it works for you. If you're the borrower, it clearly works against you.

The lender will accumulate a total of $4,163,213 if you pay him $1,000 a year for 40 years and he earns 18 percent on your payment! Is it any wonder credit card companies want you to become one of their borrowers?

Now compare the $40,000 you paid in interest over 40 years with the $767,091 you could have after earning 12 percent on $1,000 each year. WOW! Stop and think about that.

God made the greatest sacrifice by giving His Son, **Jesus Christ**, to die for us.

When you are tempted to buy something using credit, stop and think. Remind yourself of the benefits of staying out of debt.

What Does Scripture Say about Debt?

Read Romans 13:8 from several different Bible translations: *"Owe no man any thing"* (KJV); *"Let no debt remain outstanding"* (NIV); *"Pay all your debts"* (TLB); *"Keep out of debt and owe no man anything"* (AMPLIFIED).

Pretty strong words about debt, don't you think? The question is, why? Why does God so clearly discourage debt? Here are a few simple reasons.

Debt Is Slavery

In Proverbs 22:7, we read, *"Just as the rich rule the poor, so the borrower is servant to the lender"* (TLB). When we are in debt, we are servants to the lender.

In 1 Corinthians 7:23, Paul writes, *"You were bought with a price; do not become slaves of men."*

God made the greatest sacrifice by giving His Son, Jesus Christ, to die for us. And He wants us free to serve Him—not lenders.

Debt Was a Curse

In the Old Testament being out of debt was one of the rewards for obedience. *"If you diligently obey the Lord your God, being careful to do*

all His commandments . . . all these blessings will come upon you. . . . You shall lend to many nations, but you shall not borrow" (Deuteronomy 28:1-2, 12). Obeying God leads to being free from debt, not getting into it.

However becoming a borrower was one of the curses for disobedience. *"If you do not obey the Lord your God, to observe to do all His commandments . . . all these curses will come upon you. . . . The alien . . . shall lend to you, but you will not lend to him"* (Deuteronomy 28:15, 43-44).

Debt May Deny God an Opportunity

A young man wanted to go to college to become a missionary. He had no money and thought the only way he could afford college was to get a student loan. However, this would have left him with $40,000 of debt by the time he graduated, which would have been impossible to pay back on a missionary's salary.

After much prayer, he decided to enroll without the help of a student loan and to trust the Lord to meet his needs. He graduated without borrowing anything. This was the most valuable lesson learned in college as he prepared for life on the mission field.

Is there some need you have? Something you want to buy? Don't rush out and go into debt! Pray about your need or desire, and ask the Lord to show you what He wants you to do.

Is Debt Ever OK?

The Bible doesn't say when we can owe money. In some instances it may be okay to owe money for a home or business. However, if you ever borrow money, you should immediately establish the goal of paying it back as soon as possible.

Credit Cards

Remember this: Credit cards are dangerous. Not only do they cost you money through interest, but it's a proven fact that people spend more when they use credit cards instead of cash. Since they're using a little piece of plastic, they feel they're not really spending money. But they are!

Still think you want a credit card? Then use this simple rule: Unless you can pay the entire balance due at the end of each month, and avoid any interest payments, DO NOT use a credit card. If you already have a card, you should still use this rule. If you can't pay the entire balance, then I encourage you to perform some "plastic surgery." Any good pair of scissors will do.

How to Escape Auto Debt

Buying cars is one of the leading causes of debt.

If you've got a driver's license, you may already have a car loan. If that's the case, then here are some steps to get rid of this debt as quickly as possible. First, decide to keep your car for at least six years. Second, pay off your car loan. Third, when your loan is paid off, continue paying the monthly car payment, but put the money into your savings account. Then when you are ready to replace your car, the saved cash plus the trade-in value should be enough to buy your next car without credit. It may not be enough for a new car, but you should be able to purchase a good used car without any debt.

Bankruptcy

For whatever reason, sometimes a person is

unable to fulfill his or her financial obligations. This can mean late payments and fees. Or it may mean something more extreme: bankruptcy.

In bankruptcy, a judge decides if a person is unable to pay their debts, and the borrower is no longer responsible for the debt. Should a godly person declare bankruptcy? The answer is generally no. Psalm 37:21 tells us, *"The wicked borrows and does not pay back."* However, a person may be forced to take bankruptcy if a creditor isn't willing to work with him on payments he can afford, or if the debtor's emotional health is at stake.

Bankruptcy can harm people's credit rating and make it difficult for them to buy a house or start a business.

Cosigning

When you cosign on a loan, you are telling the lender that you will be responsible for paying back the loan if the person who is actually borrowing the money doesn't pay it back. It's just as if you borrowed the money and gave it to the friend who asked you to cosign.

A study found that 50 percent of those who cosigned a loan ended up making the payments.

Scripture speaks very clearly about cosigning. Proverbs 17:18 reads, *"It is poor judgment to countersign another's note, to become responsible for his debts"* (TLB). The words "poor judgment" are better translated "crazy"!

Proverbs 22:26-27 is even more graphic. It reads, *"Do not be a man who* [cosigns]. . . . *If you lack the means to pay, your very bed will be snatched from under you"* (NIV).

Some parents cosign the loan on their teen's first car. I would encourage you not to ask your parents to do this. It is far better for you to learn the importance of not going into debt. Instead, plan ahead and save your money, then buy a car when you can afford it.

Summary

The Lord discourages debt because He wants us to be free, and debt is slavery to the lender.

Put It into Practice!

Hey! Do you want to save some money?

Review the following suggestions and then write down at least three ways you think you can save money by spending more wisely.

1.) Think Yearly

``When you look at spending on a yearly basis, it gives you a much better idea of the real cost. If you eat lunch out every day and spend $3 for each meal, it does not seem like much money. But this adds up to $1,050 a year. There are many ways you can reduce spending once you understand the full cost.

2.) Food

 If possible, brown-bag your lunch at work or school. This is a good way to save on the cost of lunch and also eat nutritious meals.

 Review your eating and drinking habits. Junk food and soft drinks are expensive and can harm your health.

 It costs about 80 percent more to have a comparable meal at a fast-food restaurant than at home. When eating out, drink water for your beverage and have dessert at home.

3.) Transportation

 Buy a used automobile to save the expense of new car depreciation. Depreciation is the value a car loses as it gets older.

 If you have a car, save money by doing your errands in as few trips as possible. Walk, bike more, car pool, or use the bus or train where available. A study found that costs for an average new compact car were 47 cents a mile. The less you drive, the less you spend.

4.) Clothing

 Designer clothing is very expensive—avoid buying it! Also avoid fad clothing that is only going to be worn for a short period of time.

 Buy clothing out of season. For example, winter clothing will be on sale during the spring.

5.) Recreation

 Learn to enjoy inexpensive hobbies and sports, like hiking, time with friends, skateboarding, books from the library, and pick-up basketball games. Try not to confuse shopping with fun.

4 All pets cost money. Limit pets to those you really enjoy and can afford.

6.) Miscellaneous

4 Never buy anything through a sales call over the telephone. Many phone sales are dishonest.

4 It is much less costly to shop at thrift stores or garage sales than at an expensive mall.

"How to Save Money" Ideas:

1.) Stop buying soft drinks at the convenience store every day after school.

2.) Reduce the number of magazines I buy.

3.) Don't buy expensive "name brand" jeans.

4.) Play more basketball and see fewer movies.

My "How to Save Money" Ideas:

Chapter 4
Counsel

4 Counsel

Memorize It!

"The way of a fool is right in his own eyes, but a wise man is he who listens to counsel" (Proverbs 12:15).

Put It into Practice!

- Complete "Your Checking Account" on pages 54-57.
- Continue recording your income and spending on the worksheet on page 58.

Check It Out!

1.) Read Proverbs 12:15, Proverbs 13:10, and Proverbs 15:22.

What are some of the benefits of seeking counsel?

Proverbs 12:15

Proverbs 13:10

Proverbs 15:22

Have you ever asked someone for advice on something? What were the benefits of doing so?

What stops you from seeking counsel?

2.) Read Psalm 16:7 and Psalm 32:8.

Does the Lord counsel us?

Have you ever suffered because you didn't seek the Lord's counsel? If so, describe what happened.

How do you seek the Lord's counsel?

Read Psalm 119:105, 2 Timothy 3:16-17, and Hebrews 4:12. What do each of these verses tell us about the Scriptures?

Psalm 119:105

2 Timothy 3:16-17

Hebrews 4:12

Why should the Bible serve as your counselor?

Do you regularly read and study the Bible? If not, what prevents you?

3.) Read Proverbs 1:8-9.
Who should be among your counselors?

Who does Psalm 1:1 say would not be a good counselor?

Read Proverbs 12:5. Why should you avoid the counsel of these people?

4.) Read the Counsel Notes on pages 50-53.
What in this section particularly interested you?

Do you seek counsel when making a major financial decision? If not, how will you do so in the future?

*Please write your prayer requests in your **Prayer Log** before coming to class.*

Counsel

To Ask or Not to Ask?

Alex had been saving for years to buy a car. When he finally had enough money, he read the ads in the newspaper, then jumped up in excitement.

"This is it!" he exclaimed to his surprised parents. Then, without any further explanation, he rushed from the house.

Two hours later he was back, the proud owner of a used car. Of course, the car was almost 12 years old, covered with rust, and far from prime condition. When Alex stepped on the gas, big clouds of smoke belched out of the exhaust pipe. But Alex didn't care. He had his car.

It wasn't long before the muffler went out. Followed by the brakes. And the transmission. Finally, Alex had no choice but to sell his pride and joy to a junkyard. As the tow truck pulled away, Alex's father put his arm around his son's shoulders.

"I just have one question, son," he said quietly. "Why didn't you ask me what I thought before you bought the car?"

"Are you kidding?" Alex said. "You would have told me not to buy it!"

Two attitudes keep us from seeking counsel. The first is pride. Some people think asking advice is a sign of weakness. The second is stubbornness. This attitude is summed up in the statement, "Don't confuse me with the facts. My mind is already made up!" Like Alex, we often don't want to hear we should not purchase something we have already decided to buy. We just want to do what we want to do.

God's Word tells us to seek counsel. Proverbs 19:20 reads, *"Listen to advice and accept instruction, and in the end you will be wise"* (NIV). And Proverbs 12:15 says, *"The way of a fool is right in his own eyes, but a wise man is he who listens to counsel."*

Why Ask for Counsel?

The reason to ask someone for advice is to get help in making decisions. You're not asking anyone to make a decision for you. You're simply asking for other ideas and views. Once you receive some input, it's up to you to put it all together and come up with the final decision.

"I don't need anyone else's opinion. All I need are the facts." Plenty of people have this

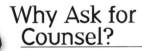
I WISH ID ASKED MY FATHER'S ADVICE.

attitude, and they find out that the facts aren't enough. Learn all you can about the decision you need to make, but don't base your decision only on the facts. You also need to know what the Lord wants you to do. This may differ from what the facts alone tell you.

Sources of Counsel

Before making an important decision, seek three sources of counsel: Scripture, godly people, and the Lord.

Scripture

The first thing to ask yourself is, What does God's Word say? The Psalmist wrote, *"Your laws are both my light and my counselors"* (119:24, TLB). In Hebrews 4:12, we read that God's Word *"is living and active … and able to judge the thoughts and intentions of the heart."* Now that's powerful. Believers in Christ have found these words to be true. We have discovered that the Bible is a living book that our Lord uses to guide us.

Did it surprise you to learn that Scripture has 2,350 verses dealing with money? Clearly, God has a lot to say about it. If the Bible tells me to do something with my money, I do it. If the Bible tells me not to do something, I don't do it. If the Bible is not clear about an issue, I go to the second source of counsel: godly people.

Godly People

"The godly man is a good counselor because he is just and fair and knows right from wrong"

(Psalm 37:30-31, TLB). Christians need to depend on one another. Nowhere is this illustrated more clearly than in Paul's discussion concerning the body of Christ in 1 Corinthians 12. Each member of the body of Christ—that's you and me—is pictured as a different part of the human body. And just like our bodies, our ability to function well as followers of Christ happens only when the members work together. God has given each of us certain abilities, but God has not given any one person all the abilities that he needs to be most productive.

So who are the godly people you can go to? Who can you ask for counsel when you need it? Well, how about your parents? Proverbs 6:20-22 says, *"My son, observe the commandment of your father and do not forsake the teaching of your mother; bind them continually on your heart; tie them around your neck. When you walk about, they will guide you; when you sleep, they will watch over you; and when you awake, they will talk to you."* I cannot tell you how much my father and mother have helped me with their counsel. Not only do they have the benefit of years of experience, but they know me well and they have my best interests at heart. Your parents can be a terrific source of wisdom and guidance, too.

Even if your folks do not yet know Christ, or if they haven't been wise money managers, ask them for counsel. Too often invisible walls are built between teenagers and their parents. When we ask our parents' advice, we are following God's instructions to honor our parents—and we begin tearing down any walls.

> "The **Bible** is a living book that **our Lord** uses to guide us."

The second source of counsel is a spouse. There probably aren't many of you who are married yet. But as you think about dating and marriage, keep in mind that when you marry, your spouse will be the first person you should talk with when decisions need to be made. My wife, Bev, has saved me a great deal of money by her wise counsel. Like many women, my wife is gifted with a wonderfully sensitive nature that is usually very accurate. Like many men, I tend to focus on the facts. When we work together, sharing ideas, we find the proper balance for a correct decision.

The third source of counsel is people with experience. Need to decide what car to buy? Find a skilled auto mechanic and ask him to check out the car before you buy it. Need to know which college to attend? Talk with people you know who are already studying in your chosen field. There are plenty of people who have worked through many of the decisions you are facing and would be glad to offer you their counsel. You can benefit from their experiences—and maybe even avoid some of the mistakes they have made!

Proverbs 15:22 reads, *"Without consultation, plans are frustrated, but with many counselors they succeed."* Each of us has limited knowledge. We need the input of others to help with choices we would never have considered without their advice.

Solomon describes the benefits of a multitude of counselors in Ecclesiastes 4:9-12: *"Two are better than one because they have a good*

> God has given us a wonderful source of information through **godly people**.

return for their labor. For if either of them falls, the one will lift up his companion. But woe to the one who falls when there is not another to lift him up. Furthermore, if two lie down together they keep warm, but how can one be warm alone? And if one can overpower him who is alone, two can resist him. A cord of three strands is not quickly torn apart."

God has given us a wonderful source of information through godly people. Don't hesitate to ask them!

The Lord

The most important source of counsel is the Lord. In Isaiah 9:6 we are told that one of the Lord's names is "Wonderful Counselor." The Psalms identify the Lord as our counselor: *"I [the Lord] will instruct you and teach you in the way which you should go; I will counsel you with My eye upon you"* (32:8).

There's a wonderful story in John 21:3-11. Peter and six of the other disciples fished all night long but caught nothing. Discouraged, they decided to stop fishing. Jesus then came and told them to cast their net once more. They obeyed and caught 153 large fish! When we know what Christ wants us to do and we obey, it is much more productive than our efforts apart from the Lord's direction.

A Bum Steer

We've talked a lot about sources of good counsel. But we also need to avoid those who will give us bad counsel. Psalm 1:1 cautions us, *"How blessed is the man who does not walk in the counsel of the wicked."* A "wicked" person is one who does not follow God.

Never Seek the Counsel of Fortune Tellers, Mediums or Spiritualists!

The Bible is very clear about this: *"Do not turn to mediums or spiritists; do not seek them out to be defiled by them. I am the Lord your God"* (Leviticus 19:31). Study this next passage carefully: *"So Saul died ... because he asked counsel of a medium, making inquiry of it, and did not inquire of the Lord. Therefore, He* [the Lord] *killed him"* (1 Chronicles 10:13-14). Saul directly disobeyed God's command. As a result, he died.

God is the only source of truth. Don't play with the occult, or even with the methods spiritists use in forecasting the future (horoscopes, Ouija boards, seances, etc.). These things are not just fun and games. They are dangerous tools of deception.

Be Careful of People Who Benefit From Giving Counsel

You need to be cautious of receiving and using counsel from a person who will make money if you carry out a certain decision. For example, a car salesman will make money only if you buy his car. So don't be misled when his counsel is completely positive and suggests that you can't live another day without his product. When receiving advice, ask yourself this question: "Will this person profit by my decision?" If the advisor will profit, always seek a second opinion.

Major Decisions—Summary

Whenever you are faced with a major decision such as a job change or car purchase, it is helpful to go to a quiet place where you can spend time reading Scripture and seeking the Lord. I encourage you to consider fasting during this time of prayer. If you're not familiar with fasting, talk with your parents or youth pastor about it.

Put It into Practice!

Your Checking Account

It won't be long before you want to open a checking account. There are two ways to deposit and withdraw funds from your checking account. The traditional way uses deposit slips and checks. Another way is to use Automatic Teller Machines and other electronic means. In this exercise we will explore the traditional method.

Opening your account

Opening a checking account is fairly simple. When you visit your bank, ask for the New Accounts Department. They will help you complete the necessary forms. One of these forms is the Signature Card, which remains on file at the bank. Only those who have signed their names on the Signature Card are authorized to write a check on your account.

When you open an account, be sure you understand the fees that may be charged to your account. Try to find a bank that won't charge you a service charge. You may need to be 18 years of age or older to open an account in your name, but the bank may let you open a joint account with your parents.

Making a deposit (adding money to your account)

After you have opened your account, you will be given your first deposit slip to enter the amount of money you want to put into your account. A similar slip will be used each time you put money into your account. After you have deposited your money, you will be given a receipt for your records. Always keep your receipts. In case of a mistake, you have proof of your deposit.

Your bank will send you a monthly record of processed deposits and checks (often you'll have the option of receiving this information online). You will find a series of numbers on the bottom of your checks. These numbers are printed with a special ink that allows computers to read them.

Examine John's deposit on page 56. He opened his account with a check for $125, $22 in cash and $1.25 in coins. The total deposit was $148.25.

Writing a check

Look at the sample of a check on page 56. There are five steps in filling out a check:

1.) Enter the date.
2.) Enter the name of the person or company to whom the check is to be paid.
3.) Enter in figures the amount of the check.
4.) Write out the amount of the check in words. All amounts are written in dollars and fractions of dollars. John's check for $15.75 is written "Fifteen dollars and 75/100."
5.) Sign the check the same way you signed the Signature Card.

Always write the checks clearly in ink. Never use a pencil. (To help you remember later what the check was for, make a note on the line designated for that purpose.)

Recording your deposits and checks

Each deposit and each check written should be described in a "Checking Account Register." Take as many lines as you need to describe each transaction. Maintain a running balance so you will always know how much money remains in your checking account.

For Deposits: Record the date, write the abbreviation for deposit (DEP) in the "check number" column, describe your deposit and the amount. Then add the deposit to your balance.

For Checks Written: Record the date, check number, description, and the amount of the check. Then subtract the amount of the check from the existing balance to find the new balance.

Review the sample Checking Account Register at the bottom of page 56.

For ATM Transactions: In the same way you record your paper deposits and checks, be sure to note each ATM deposit or withdrawal in your register so that you'll have an accurate record of your account balance. Include any fees that may be involved.

Balancing your monthly bank account statement

You must balance your Checking Account Register with the monthly statement the bank sends you to make sure neither you nor the bank made an error. This is called reconciling. Do this as soon as you receive the statement. Yes, a bank can make a mistake.

First, compare the information on each check and deposit with the entry in your check register and with the bank statement. If all three agree, place a check mark in the proper column of the check register. In the example on page 56, the first deposit and check numbers 101 and 102 have been verified. A check mark has been placed to confirm that each is correct.

After you have verified each transaction, the balance in your check book register should agree with the balance on the bank statement. If there is a difference, check for a mistake in addition or subtraction. Should you need any additional help, the bank will assist you. (If you have online access to your account, it's a good idea to periodically review your account activity to be sure there are no irregularities.)

This week's exercise:

1.) **Fill out the blank deposit slip** on page 57 for a $136.75 check, $12 in cash and $9.34 in coins.
2.) **Complete the blank check** on page 57 for $65.50 to Friendly Automobile Repair.
3.) **Enter both of these** on the check register on page 57.

Deposit

John Stevens
30 Easy Street
Anywhere, U.S.A.

DATE _1-15-2005_

ALL ITEMS ARE RECEIVED BY THIS BANK FOR THE PURPOSES OF COLLECTION AND ARE SUBJECT TO PROVISIONS OF THE UNIFORM COMMERCIAL CODE WHERE APPLICABLE AND THE RULES AND REGULATIONS OF THIS BANK. ALL CREDITS FOR ITEMS ARE PROVISIONAL UNTIL COLLECTED.

LAST NATIONAL BANK

⑆0515⑈001 01851⑆ 00 0000 00

CURRENCY	22	00
COIN	1	25
C H E C K S	125	00
TOTAL FROM OTHER SIDE		
TOTAL	148	25
LESS CASH RECEIVED		
Total Deposit	148	25

102

69-185 / 515

DEPOSIT TICKET
PLEASE ITEMIZE ADDITIONAL CHECKS ON REVERSE SIDE

SIGN HERE ONLY IF CASH RECEIVED FROM DEPOSIT

Check

John Stevens
30 Easy Street
Anywhere, U.S.A.

101

DATE _1-16-2005_

69-185 / 515

PAY TO THE ORDER OF _First Church_ $ _15.75_

Fifteen and 75/100 _____ DOLLARS

LAST NATIONAL BANK

FOR _Give to Lord_   _John Stevens_

⑆0515⑈001 01851⑆ 00 0000 00

Checking Account Register

BE SURE TO DEDUCT ANY PER CHECK CHARGES OR MAINTENANCE CHARGES THAT MAY APPLY.

DATE	CHECK NUMBER	CHECKS ISSUED TO OR DEPOSITS RECEIVED FROM	AMOUNT OF DEPOSIT	AMOUNT OF CHECK	T	BALANCE
1 15	DEP	Open Account	148 25		4	148 25
1 16	101	First Church (Giving)		15 75	4	132 50
1 30	102	Friendly Auto (Repairs)		25 00	4	107 50
2 3	DEP	Job Income	125 00			232 50

Deposit

John Stevens
30 Easy Street
Anywhere, U.S.A.

DATE _____

ALL ITEMS ARE RECEIVED BY THIS BANK FOR THE PURPOSES OF COLLECTION AND ARE SUBJECT TO PROVISIONS OF THE UNIFORM COMMERCIAL CODE WHERE APPLICABLE AND THE RULES AND REGULATIONS OF THIS BANK. ALL CREDITS FOR ITEMS ARE PROVISIONAL UNTIL COLLECTED.

LAST NATIONAL BANK

CURRENCY			102
COIN			
CHECKS			69-185 / 515
TOTAL FROM OTHER SIDE			
TOTAL			**DEPOSIT TICKET**
LESS CASH RECEIVED			PLEASE ITEMIZE ADDITIONAL CHECKS ON REVERSE SIDE
Total Deposit			

SIGN HERE ONLY IF CASH RECEIVED FROM DEPOSIT

⑂:0515 001 0185⑆:   00   0000   00

Check

John Stevens
30 Easy Street
Anywhere, U.S.A.

101

DATE _____

69-185 / 515

PAY TO THE ORDER OF _____ $ _____

_____ DOLLARS

LAST NATIONAL BANK

FOR _____

⑂:0515 001 0185⑆:   00   0000   00

Checking Account Register

BE SURE TO DEDUCT ANY PER CHECK CHARGES OR MAINTENANCE CHARGES THAT MAY APPLY.

DATE	CHECK NUMBER	CHECKS ISSUED TO OR DEPOSITS RECEIVED FROM	AMOUNT OF DEPOSIT	AMOUNT OF CHECK	T	BALANCE

Recording Your Income & Spending

Description	Amounts	Totals for Third Week
Income		
Giving		
Savings		
Food		
School/Lessons		
Clothing		
Grooming		
Transportation		
Sports		
Entertainment		
Gifts		
Other:		
Other:		

Chapter **5**

Honesty

Honesty

Memorize It!

"You shall not steal, nor deal falsely, nor lie to one another" (Leviticus 19:11).

Put It into Practice!

- Continue recording your income and spending on the worksheet on page 70.
- Complete the "Estimated Budget" on pages 71-73.

Check It Out!

 1.) Read Leviticus 19:11-13, Deuteronomy 25:13-16, and Ephesians 4:25.

What do these verses say about God's demand for honesty?

Leviticus 19:11-13

Deuteronomy 25:13-16

Ephesians 4:25

Are you honest in even the smallest matters? If not, what will you do to change?

What are two factors that influence us to act dishonestly?

1.)

2.)

2.) Read Exodus 18:21-22.

Why does the Lord require honesty in leaders?

According to Proverbs 14:2, can you practice dishonesty and still love God? Why or why not?

What do Proverbs 26:28 and Romans 13:9-10 have to say about practicing dishonesty and still loving your neighbor?

3.) Read Psalm 15:1-5 and Proverbs 12:22.

List some of the benefits of honesty.

Psalm 15:1-5	

Proverbs 12:22	

Read Proverbs 3:32 and Proverbs 21:6. What are some of the curses of dishonesty?

> *Proverbs 3:32*

> *Proverbs 21:6*

Define restitution:

What does Exodus 22:1-4 say about restitution?

If you have gotten anything dishonestly, what do you need to do?

What is a bribe?

What does Exodus 23:8 say about bribes?

4.) Read the Honesty Notes on pages 64-69.

How does the example of Abraham in Genesis 14:21-23 challenge you to be honest even in small things?

Ask the Lord to show you any areas of dishonesty in your life. Write below at least three things you will do to deal with those areas.

*Please write your prayer requests in your **Prayer Log** before coming to class.*

Honesty

Cindy received her paycheck...

and was delighted to see she'd received $50 more than usual. Rather than question the difference, she simply deposited it.

The next week she was upset to see her paycheck was $50 less than usual!

She stormed into her boss's office and informed him she was $50 short.

"Funny," he replied. "You didn't complain last week when you received $50 too much."

"Well, of course not!" Cindy huffed. "I can overlook one mistake, but when you mess up twice I just have to speak up!"

What would you have done in this circumstance? Would you have told your boss he'd made an error and paid you too much? Do you tell the cashier at the store when you receive too much change? Have you ever tried to sell something and been tempted not to tell the truth about the item because you might lose the sale?

Honesty is not easy, especially in our world today. It seems as though movies, TV shows, books, and magazines encourage you to "Look out for #1," even if that means lying.

But Scripture doesn't agree with that philosophy. God demands total honesty. Proverbs 20:23 reads, *"The Lord loathes all cheating and dishonesty"* (TLB). Proverbs 6:16-17 states, *"The Lord hates ... a lying tongue."*

In God's view, lying has no place in our lives.

The God of Truth

The Lord is identified as the God of truth. John 14:6 tells us, *"I [God] am ... the truth."* Now, take a look at what the Bible has to say about Satan: *"He [the devil] ... does not stand in the truth, because there is no truth in him. Whenever he speaks a lie, he speaks from his own nature, for he is a liar and the father of lies"* (John 8:44).

Do you want to be a reflection of God's character? Then deal with others honestly. If you don't do

ISSUE	SCRIPTURE	SOCIETY
Standard of honesty:	Absolute	Relative
God's concern about honesty:	He demands honesty	There is no God
The decision to be honest or dishonest is based upon:	Faith in the invisible living God	Only the facts that can be seen
Question usually asked when deciding to be honest:	Will it please God?	Will I get away with it?

this, you will be reflecting the dishonest nature of the devil.

So what's the big deal? Why does God demand honesty? For Here are several important reasons!

We Cannot Practice Dishonesty and Love God

Jesus told us, *"If you love Me, you will keep My commandments"* (John 14:15). We cannot love God if we are not keeping His commands to be honest.

When you act dishonestly, you are acting as though the living God doesn't even exist! You buy into the lie that God is not able to provide exactly what you need, even though He has promised to do so (Matthew 6:33). You decide to take care of yourself your own dishonest way.

But guess what? Dishonesty may seem to work in the short term, but later it leads to disaster. Remember, God knows everything about you! Don't fool yourself by thinking He won't notice if you disobey Him—or that He won't discipline you. Like any good parent, God will correct us when we are disobedient.

Honest behavior is an act of faith. When you make the decision to be honest, those around you may think you're pretty foolish. Can you imagine how some of your friends who don't know Jesus might react if you tell a clerk he has given you too much change? They'd probably think you'd lost your mind. But the godly person considers another factor that friends can't see: Jesus Christ. Every honest

> Every **honest decision** you make helps you grow stronger in your faith.

decision you make helps you grow stronger in your faith and brings you closer to Christ. Remember, *"He who walks in his uprightness fears the Lord, but he who is crooked in his ways despises Him"* (Proverbs 14:2). Dishonesty leads to hating God!

We Cannot Practice Dishonesty and Love Our Neighbor

The second reason the Lord demands honesty is because dishonesty breaks the second commandment: *"You shall love your neighbor as yourself"* (Mark 12:31). Romans 13:9-10 reads, *"If you love your neighbor as much as you love yourself you will not want to harm or cheat him, or kill him or steal from him.... Love does no wrong to anyone"* (TLB).

"I would never be dishonest and steal!" you say. Maybe not, but many people who consider themselves completely honest steal every day. They come to work late or leave early, which is stealing time from their employers. They take little things—like a few fries out of a warming bin—from the companies for which they work. It's easy to tell yourself you're stealing from a business, but that's not the whole truth. Every time you take something from work that doesn't belong to you, you steal from other people. Business owners or taxpayers have to pay for your theft.

And, whether you know it or not—you are

stealing from yourself as well. You are stealing the blessings you would be receiving from God for being obedient.

You can always count on this fact: Dishonesty always hurts people—even the ones being dishonest.

Dishonesty Hurts Our Witness for Christ

Our Lord demands honesty because that demonstrates the reality of Jesus Christ to those around us who don't yet know Him.

I will never forget the first time I told a neighbor how he could come to know Christ as his Savior. His face turned red as he snarled, "Well, I know a person who talks a lot about Jesus, but watch out if you ever try to buy anything from him! He'd cheat his own mother! If that's what it means to be a Christian, I don't want any part of it!"

Our actions speak louder than our words. You may be the only "Bible" your friends read. Philippians 2:15 says, *"Prove yourselves to be blameless and innocent, children of God above reproach in the midst of a crooked and perverse generation, among whom you appear as lights in the world."*

We can influence people for Jesus Christ by handling our money honestly. Robert had been trying to sell a pickup truck for months. Finally, a man decided to buy the truck. At the last moment, however, he said, "I'll buy this truck, but

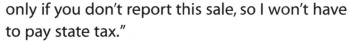

only if you don't report this sale, so I won't have to pay state tax."

Robert said, "I'm sorry, I can't do that because Jesus Christ is my Lord." Robert later said, "You should have seen his face. He almost went into shock! Then an interesting thing happened. His attitude completely changed. Not only did he buy the truck, but rarely have I seen anyone as open to knowing Jesus Christ."

Honesty Confirms God's Direction

Proverbs 4:24, 26 reads, *"Put away from you a deceitful mouth, and put devious speech far from you … and all your ways will be established."* What a helpful principle! When you practice honesty, "all your ways will be established." When you honor God by living your life with honesty, He can—and will—honor you by keeping His promises to guide you.

Even the Smallest Act of Dishonesty Is Harmful

Dishonesty in small things leads to dishonesty in bigger things. *"Whoever is dishonest with very little will also be dishonest with much"* (Luke 16:10, NIV).

Reading about Abraham has taught me a great deal about being honest in small things. In Genesis 14, the king of Sodom offered Abraham all the goods Abraham recovered when he returned from successfully rescuing the people of Sodom. But Abraham responded to the king, *"I have sworn to the Lord God Most High, possessor of heaven and earth, that I will not take a thread or a sandal thong or anything that is yours"* (Genesis 14:22-23).

Seems a bit extreme, doesn't it? I mean, Abraham had fought a hard battle to rescue these people and the things that had been stolen. But Abraham had made a pledge to God that he wasn't going to take so much as a thread or a sandal thong!

I challenge you to make a similar commitment. Commit not to steal a stamp or a pencil or a paper clip or food or a penny from anyone. Stop and decide right now, today, that you will be honest in all matters at home, in school, at your job … anywhere you are.

Temptations—Don't Give In!

OK, so you've decided to follow God's command to be honest. Does that mean you'll never be tempted again to cheat or tell a lie? Not at all. So how do you resist the temptations you will face?

1.) By the Power of the Holy Spirit

A friend was teaching about honesty to a class when one person said, "I think we all would like to be honest. But I know that if the right opportunity comes along, I'm going to be dishonest or cheat on tests." I think that student was correct. We all will give in to temptation, unless we are yielded to the Holy Spirit.

This is confirmed by Galatians 5:16-17: *"Live by the Spirit, and you will not gratify the desires of the sinful nature. For the sinful nature desires what is contrary to the Spirit, and the Spirit what is contrary to the sinful nature"* (NIV). Mark 7:21-22 adds, *"Out of men's hearts, come evil thoughts … theft … deceit"* (NIV).

The desire of our human nature is to act dishonestly. But the desire of the Spirit is for us to be honest. We must submit ourselves entirely to Jesus Christ as Lord and allow Him to live His life through us.

What does this mean? That we don't have to make right decisions on our own! God is here, ready to help us. And the Holy Spirit is within us, just waiting to encourage us to follow God's directions. We don't have to do it alone, but we do have to be willing to let the Father work in our hearts.

2.) By Practicing the Golden Rule

You've probably heard it a million times. "Do unto others as you would have them do unto you." Philippians 2:4 takes it a step further: *"Do not merely look out for your own personal interests, but also for the interests of others."*

When you have a question about how you should treat someone, answer this simple question: "If I were the other person, how would I want to be treated?" Let kindness and truth be your guides. They won't let you down.

3.) By a Healthy Fear of the Lord

When I talk of a "healthy fear" of the Lord, I do not mean that God is a bully just waiting for the opportunity to punish us. Not at all! Our God is a loving Father who, out of infinite love, disciplines His children for their benefit. *"He disciplines us for our good, so that we may share His holiness"* (Hebrews 12:10).

One of the methods God uses to motivate us to honest living is this "healthy fear." Proverbs 16:6 reads, *"By the fear of the Lord one keeps away from evil."* Let me illustrate how the fear of the Lord helps us act honestly.

Once, while on a trip, I shared a motel room with a friend. As we were leaving the next morning, he took one of the motel's towels and walked to the car. Suddenly I was overwhelmed by the fear of the Lord. What came to my mind was Hebrews 12:11: *"All discipline for the moment seems not to be joyful, but sorrowful."*

Discipline hurts! I would rather obey Him than to make a decision that would lead my loving Father to discipline me. I was afraid for my friend and for myself. I told him of my fear and was relieved when he returned the towel!

I believe that our heavenly Father will not allow us to keep anything we have acquired dishonestly. Proverbs 13:11 reads, *"Wealth obtained by fraud dwindles."* A friend purchased four plants but the clerk only charged her for one. She knew it, but she left the store anyway without paying for the other three. She said it was simply miraculous how quickly three of those plants died!

What if We Blow it?

Unfortunately, from time to time, everyone acts dishonestly. That's just a fact of life. So what do you do when you realize you've disobeyed God's commands regarding honesty?

First, restore your fellowship with God.

Sin builds walls between us and the Lord. When your fellowship with the Father has been damaged, you need to restore it. The Bible tells us how to do this in 1 John 1:9: *"If we confess our sins, He is faithful and righteous to forgive us our sins and to cleanse us from all unrighteousness."*

We must agree with God that our dishonesty was sin, and then accept God's forgiveness so we can again enjoy His fellowship.

Second, restore your fellowship with the person with whom you were dishonest.

Follow the guidance from James 5:16 to *"confess your sins to one another."* Tell the person you have hurt what you did.

This won't be easy. It's painful for you and the person against whom you've sinned. I've

had only a few people confess that they have wronged me. Interestingly, these people have become my closest friends, in part because of my respect for them. They wanted an honest relationship with me so much that they were willing to expose their sins.

If this sounds impossible, you're not alone. This has been very hard for me. For the first time, several years ago, I went to someone I had wronged and confessed my sin. But the amazing thing was that afterward I sensed great freedom. That old cliché is true: Confession really is good for the soul . . . and for your peace of mind.

Third, return any stolen property.

If you have stolen something, you must return it to its owner with something extra. This is called restitution. *"He shall restore what he took by robbery . . . or anything about which he swore falsely; he shall make restitution for it in full and add to it one-fifth more"* (Leviticus 6:4-5).

Restitution is a way to say, "I am sorry. Please forgive me." Zaccheus is a good example of fulfilling this principle. He promised Jesus, *"If I have defrauded anyone of anything, I will give back four times as much"* (Luke 19:8).

Honesty Starts at the Top

The Lord is especially concerned with the honesty of leaders. Why? Simple—because they influence their followers.

The owner of a business began wearing cowboy boots to work. Within six months, all the men in his office wore boots. He suddenly changed to business shoes and six months later all the men were wearing business shoes.

In a similar way, a dishonest leader produces dishonest followers. *"If a ruler pays atten-*

tion to falsehood, all his ministers become wicked" (Proverbs 29:12).

If you are in a position of leadership, lead by example. Let your followers see that you deal with everyone honestly.

Bribes

Have you ever had anyone offer you a bribe? A bribe is given to a person to influence him to do something illegal or wrong. Don't take it. You should never take a bribe: *"You shall not take a bribe, for a bribe blinds the clear-sighted and subverts the cause of the just"* (Exodus 23:8).

Blessings and Curses

The Bible is clear about honesty and what it brings. It is equally clear about the consequences of dishonesty. The verses below show some of the blessings promised for the honest and the curses the dishonest will experience. Read these slowly and ask God to use them to motivate you to a life of honesty.

Summary

It's clear that God wants you to be totally honest! There is no alternative. Lies, cheating in class, stealing . . . none of this is acceptable in God's eyes. In your relationships, in your job, and at school, the only thing that will please the Lord is honesty.

The good news is you don't have to be honest by yourself. God has given you the Holy Spirit to help you. You can go into each day knowing that you can handle money in a way that will honor Him—and that will open the door for God to give the blessings He has waiting for you!

Blessings Promised for the Honest

- **Blessing of a closer relationship with the Lord** – *"The devious are an abomination to the Lord; but He is intimate with the upright"* (Proverbs 3:32).

- **Blessings on the family** – *"A righteous man who walks in his integrity—how blessed are his sons after him"* (Proverbs 20:7).

- **Blessings of life** – *"Truthful lips will be established forever, but a lying tongue is only for a moment"* (Proverbs 12:19).

- **Blessings of prosperity** – *"Great wealth is in the house of the righteous . . ."* (Proverbs 15:6).

Curses Reserved for the Dishonest

- **Curse of not being close to God** – *"The devious are an abomination to the Lord"* (Proverbs 3:32).

- **Curse on the family** – *"He who profits illicitly troubles his own house . . ."* (Proverbs 15:27).

- **Curse of death** – *"The acquisition of treasures by a lying tongue is a fleeting vapor, the pursuit of death"* (Proverbs 21:6).

- **Curse of poverty** – *"Wealth obtained by fraud dwindles"* (Proverbs 13:11).

Recording Your Income & Spending

Description	Amounts	Totals for Fourth Week
Income		
Giving		
Savings		
Food		
School/Lessons		
Clothing		
Grooming		
Transportation		
Sports		
Entertainment		
Gifts		
Other:		
Other:		

Put It into Practice!

Your Estimated Budget

Keep recording your income and spending for the fourth week (page 70). The next step is to complete the Estimated Budget on page 73. This is an estimate of your income and spending.

How to Complete the Estimated Budget

1.) Enter the weekly income and spending.

Enter in the Estimated Budget the weekly totals form each category from your weekly "Recording Your Income & Spending" worksheets. You may have to guess what your income and spending is for the fourth week.

2.) Add the weekly totals.

Add the weekly totals in each category to determine your monthly totals.

3.) Adjust your budget.

Study the totals in each category. Adjust any of the totals that re not an average month. For example, you may have spent more for gifts than normal if it is Christmas season.

4.) Determine the surplus or deficit of your budget.

Add all the totals from the spending categories. Then subtract this from your income to find out if you are spending more money than you are receiving.

If you find out that you are spending more than your income, you must adjust your budget until it balances. You must either increase income or reduce spending.

The best way to balance the budget is to review each category and ask yourself these two questions about each spending category:

3 **Do I really need this?**

3 **Can I buy this less expensively?**

Some decisions will be hard to make. It's not easy to reduce spending. But the blessing of having a balanced budget is worth the struggle.

Estimated Budget

Description	Totals for First Week	Totals for Second Week	Totals for Third Week	Totals for Fourth Week	Totals for Month
Income	13.50	8.75	20.25	15.00	57.50
Giving	3.50	1.00	3.25	2.00	9.75
Savings	2.00	.90	2.10	2.25	7.25
Food	3.00	1.25	4.50	1.75	10.50
School/Lessons	0	0	0	0	0
Clothing	0	0	9.50	0	9.50
Grooming	2.50	0	1.25	0	3.75
Transportation	.50	0	.50	0	1.00
Sports	0	0	5.00	0	5.00
Entertainment	3.00	2.50	0	1.00	6.50
Gifts	0	0	3.25	0	3.25
Other:	0	0	0	0	0
Other:	0	0	0	0	0

Determine the surplus or deficit of your budget:

Income	+	57.50
Subtract Spending	–	56.50
Equals Surplus or Deficit	=	1.00

Estimated Budget

Description	Totals for First Week	Totals for Second Week	Totals for Third Week	Totals for Fourth Week	Totals for Month
Income					
Giving					
Savings					
Food					
School/Lessons					
Clothing					
Grooming					
Transportation					
Sports					
Entertainment					
Gifts					
Other:					
Other:					

Determine the surplus or deficit of your budget:

Income + _____

Subtract Spending − _____

Equals Surplus or Deficit = _____

Chapter 6

Giving

Chapter 6 — Giving

Memorize It!

"Remember the words of the Lord Jesus, that He Himself said, 'It is more blessed to give than to receive'" (Acts 20:35).

Put It into Practice!

- Complete "Beginning Your Budget" on page 85.

Check It Out!

1.) Read 1 Corinthians 13:3 and 2 Corinthians 9:7.

What do they say about giving with a proper attitude?

1 Corinthians 13:3

2 Corinthians 9:7

How would you describe your attitude about giving?

How is the principle in Acts 20:35 different from the way most people think about giving?

List the benefits for the giver which are found in the following passages:

Proverbs 11:24-25

Matthew 6:20

Luke 12:34

2.) How would you define the tithe?

According to Malachi 3:8-10, was the tithe required under Old Testament Law?

Read 2 Corinthians 8:1-5. Answer the following questions:

What was the financial condition of the churches in Macedonia?

How would you describe their giving?

What step in verse 5 did they take that allowed them to give so generously?

What can you learn from studying their example?

What do Galatians 6:6 and 1 Timothy 5:17-18 tell you about giving to your church and to those who teach the Scriptures?

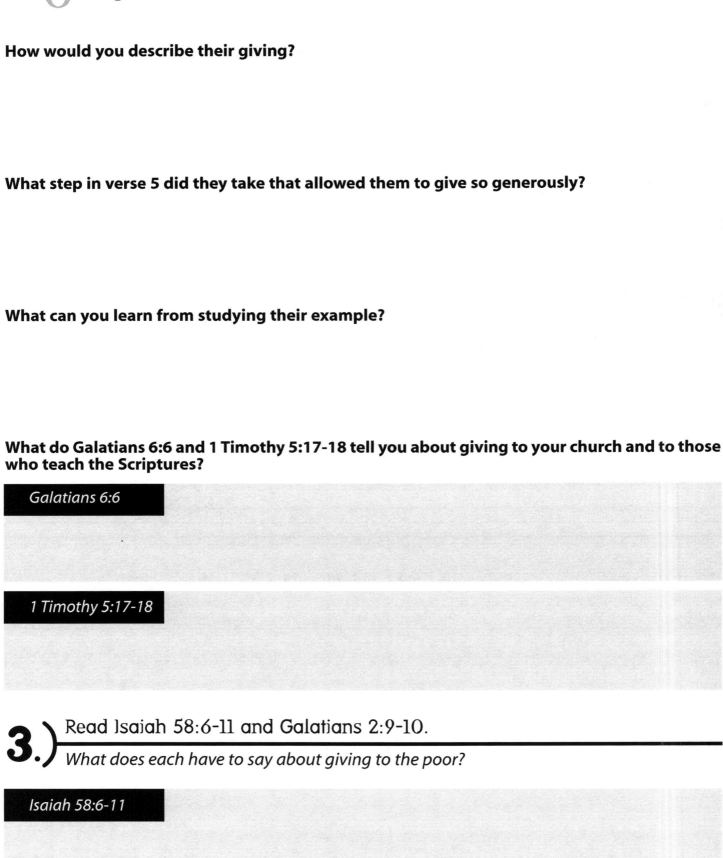

Galatians 6:6

1 Timothy 5:17-18

3.) Read Isaiah 58:6-11 and Galatians 2:9-10.

What does each have to say about giving to the poor?

Isaiah 58:6-11

Galatians 2:9-10

Study Matthew 25:35-45. How does Jesus Christ identify with the poor?

Are you currently giving to the poor? If not, what is hindering you?

4.) Read the Giving Notes on pages 80-84.

Share what you learned about giving that proved especially interesting.

How will this affect your giving?

*Please write your prayer requests in your **Prayer Log** before coming to class.*

Giving

Few areas of the Christian life...

can be more frustrating than that of giving. For several years after I met Christ, I did not want to give. After all, I'd worked hard for my money, and there were a lot of things I wanted to do with it. Why should I give to the church?

Then I took a look at what the Scriptures teach about giving.

Have an Attitude

God judges our actions by our attitude. Look at the Lord's attitude in giving: *"For God so loved the world, that He gave His only begotten Son"* (John 3:16). Because God loved, He gave. He set the example of giving motivated by love.

An attitude of love in giving is important. Consider 1 Corinthians 13:3: *"If I give all my possessions to feed the poor ... but do not have love, it profits me nothing."* It's hard to think of anything more generous than giving everything to the poor. But if it is done without love, it is of no benefit to the giver.

According to God your attitude is more important than how much you give. Jesus said in Matthew 23:23: *"Woe to you, scribes and Pharisees, hypocrites! For you tithe mint and dill and cummin, and have neglected the weightier provisions of the law: justice and mercy and faithfulness; but these are the things you should have done without neglecting the others."*

The Pharisees had been careful to give the correct amount—down to the last mint leaf in their gardens! But because of their wrong attitude, Christ rebuked them. Do you want your giving to be valuable in God's eyes? Do it from a heart of love.

Giving from a heart of love becomes possible when we recognize that our gifts are actually given to the Lord Himself, even though people receive them. An example of this is found in Numbers 18:24: *"For the tithe of the sons of Israel, which they offer as an offering to the Lord, I have given to the Levites."*

If giving is just to a church, a ministry or some needy person, it is only charity. But if it is to the Lord, it becomes an act of worship. Because God is our Creator, our Savior, and our faithful Provider, we can express our love by giving our gifts to Him. For example, when the offering plate is being passed at church, we should remind ourselves that we are giving our gift to the Lord Himself.

In addition to giving out of a heart filled

with love, we are to give cheerfully. *"God loves a cheerful giver"* (2 Corinthians 9:7). The key to cheerful giving is to submit yourself to Christ, asking Him to direct how much He wants you to give.

Stop and examine yourself. What is your attitude toward giving?

Gaining by Giving

Clearly a gift benefits the one who receives it. The local church continues its ministry, the hungry are fed, and missionaries are sent. But according to the Lord, if a gift is given with the right attitude, the giver benefits more than the receiver. *"Remember the words of the Lord Jesus, that He Himself said, 'It is more blessed to give than to receive'"* (Acts 20:35). When you give, you benefit in four ways.

You Grow Closer to God

Giving directs our heart to Christ. Matthew 6:21 tells us, *"For where your treasure is, there your heart will be also."* This is why it is so necessary to give each gift to Jesus Christ. When you give your gift to Him, your heart will be drawn to the Lord.

You Grow More Like Christ

Our heavenly Father wants our character to be like that of Jesus. Christ is an unselfish giver. Unfortunately, humans have a selfish nature. One of the ways we become more like Christ is by regular giving. Someone once said, "Giving is not God's way of raising money; it is God's way of raising people to be more like His Son."

You Grow in Heaven

Matthew 6:20 reads, *"But store up for yourselves treasures in heaven, where neither moth*

nor rust destroys, and where thieves do not break in and steal."

The Lord tells us that there really is something like the "First National Bank of Heaven." Paul wrote, *"Not that I seek the gift itself, but I seek for the profit which increases to your account"* (Philippians 4:17). When we give, we make deposits in our account in heaven which we will enjoy forever.

You Grow on Earth

Giving can result in material blessings. Proverbs 11:24-25 reads, *"There is one who scatters, and yet increases all the more.... The generous man will be prosperous, and he who waters will himself be watered."*

Check out 2 Corinthians 9:6, 8-10: *"He who sows sparingly will also reap sparingly, and he who sows bountifully will also reap bountifully.... God is able to make all grace abound to you, so that always having all sufficiency in everything, you may have an abundance for every good deed; as it is written, 'He scattered abroad, He gave to the poor.' ... He who supplies seed to the sower and bread for food, will supply and multiply your seed for sowing."*

These verses teach that giving often results in a material increase. Look again at the kinds of benefits listed: *"shall also reap bountifully ... always having all sufficiency in everything ... may*

have an abundance ... will supply and multiply your seed." Pretty impressive!

But note carefully why the Lord is giving back to those who give to Him: *"You may have an abundance for every good deed.... [The Lord] will supply and multiply your seed for sowing."* As shown in the diagram, the Lord often produces a material increase so that we may give more and have our needs met at the same time. Study the cycle in giving. When we give, we should do so expecting the Lord to provide an increase, but not knowing when or how the Lord may choose to provide this increase. In my experience I have found that He can be very creative!

Remember, you can receive the advantages of giving only when you give cheerfully out of a heart of love.

How Much?

Let's look at what the Scriptures say about how much to give.

Under the Old Testament law a tithe was required. A tithe is 10 percent of a person's income. The Lord condemns the children of Israel in Malachi 3:8-9 for not tithing: *"Will a man rob God? Yet you are robbing Me! But you say, 'How have we robbed You?' In tithes and offerings. You are cursed with a curse, for you are robbing Me."*

But giving in the Old Testament didn't end with the tithe. God also asked His people to make offerings. What's more, the Lord had special laws to help the poor.

The New Testament teaches us to give in

proportion to the income we've received. And it gives special praise for sacrificial giving.

So how much should I give?

To answer this question, first submit yourself to the Lord. Ask Him to give you clear direction. Our family is convinced that we should tithe as a minimum and then give over and above the tithe as the Lord prospers and directs us.

Karissa didn't have much money. She hadn't found a job for the summer, so her only income was her allowance. She tithed 10 percent of that, but she wished she could do more. Then she saw a notice in the church newsletter asking for volunteers to provide day care during a church event. She called the coordinator and, before she knew it, she was in a church classroom surrounded by three-year-olds. And she had the time of her life! Not so much because she liked to baby-sit, but because she'd found a way to give something back to God.

You may be in a similar situation. Money is one thing you can give, but it's not the only thing. Not everyone has money to give, but it's a fact that everyone can give a part of himself or herself! Remember what the greatest Giver of all time gave: His only Son.

So Many Needs, So Little Cash!

Once I saw all the instructions in Scripture about giving to the Lord, I wanted to give. But there was another problem: There were lots of needs—my church, the poor, missionaries, other ministries—and I did not have enough money

Giving

Material Increase

Needs Met

to meet all those needs. How could I decide where I should give?

Let's take a look at some possibilities.

The Local Church, Christian Workers, and Ministries

The Bible tells us to support those in ministry. The Old Testament priests were to receive support: *"To the sons of Levi, behold, I have given all the tithe in Israel ... in return for their service"* (Numbers 18:21). And the New Testament teaching on such support is just as strong: *"Pastors who do their work well should be paid well and should be highly appreciated, especially those who work hard at both preaching and teaching"* (1 Timothy 5:17, TLB).

People ask me if we give only through our church. In our case, the answer is no. We give a minimum of 10 percent of our regular income to our church, but we also give to others who teach us. *"The one who is taught the word is to share all good things with the one who teaches him"* (Galatians 6:6).

The Poor

Matthew 25:34-45 is one of the most exciting and yet sobering passages in Scripture. Read this carefully: *"Then the King will say ... 'I was hungry, and you gave Me something to eat; I was thirsty, and you gave Me something to drink.' ... The righteous will answer Him, 'Lord, when did we see You hungry, and feed You, or thirsty, and give You something to drink?' ... The King will answer ... 'To the extent that you did it to one of these brothers of Mine, even the least of them, you did it to Me.' Then He will also say to those on His left, 'Depart from Me, accursed ones, into the eternal fire. ... I was hungry, and you gave Me nothing to eat; I was thirsty, and you gave Me nothing to drink. ... To the extent that you did not do it to one of the least of these, you did not do it to Me.'"*

In some way we cannot fully understand, when we share with the poor, we are actually sharing with Jesus. And when we do not give to the poor, we leave Christ hungry and thirsty.

After Paul met with the disciples, he said: *"They [the disciples] only asked us to remember the poor—the very thing I also was eager to do"* (Galatians 2:10).

There must have been dozens of subjects the disciples could have discussed with Paul, but the only one they mentioned was to remember the poor. Now that should tell us something! Two areas of our life are affected by giving to the poor: prayer and having our needs met.

Prayer

Do you ever feel as though God is sticking His fingers in His ears and not listening to your prayers? A lack of giving to the poor could be affecting your prayers.

Isaiah 58:7, 9 says: *"Divide your bread with the hungry.... Then you will call, and the Lord will answer,"* and Proverbs 21:13 reads: *"He who shuts his ear to the cry of the poor will also cry himself and not be answered."*

Having Our Needs Met

Ever heard the saying, "What goes around, comes around"? If you want your needs to be met, you need to obey God. And that means giving to the needy. *"He who gives to the poor will never want, but he who shuts his eyes will have many curses"* (Proverbs 28:27).

Please consider asking the Lord to bring one poor person into your life; you can do so by praying this prayer: "God, give me the desire to share with the poor. Bring a poor person into my life so that I might learn what it really means to give." This will be an important step for you to grow in your relationship with Christ.

A friend of ours prayed this prayer after he went through the Crown Adult Study. In a matter of weeks the Lord sent a young inner-city boy for him to help. The boy's father and most of his family were in prison. Our friend continued to help the boy for a long time and took him into his home to live. The boy is almost an adult now, and the love and concern our friend has given him has forever changed both their lives—all of this because of a prayer to help one poor person.

I pray that you and I might be able to say with Job: *"I delivered the poor who cried for help, and the orphan who had no helper.... I made the*

> Consider asking the Lord to bring one **poor person** into your life.

widow's heart sing for joy.... I was eyes to the blind and feet to the lame. I was a father to the needy" (Job 29:12-13, 15-16).

Although giving can be frustrating at times, the benefits for the giver make it one of the most exciting areas in the Christian life.

What about Secular Charities?

Many secular charities (such as schools or organizations that fight diseases) compete for our gift dollars. My wife and I have decided not to support these organizations with our gifts on a regular basis. Our reason is that while many people support these charities, only those who know the Lord support the ministries of Christ. We have occasionally given to secular charities when asked by a friend we wanted to influence for Christ or when we sensed that the Lord wanted us to give.

Summary

You will experience few things as wonderful as learning to give. No matter what else you think about giving, always remember this: Give cheerfully out of a heart of love, because you are really giving to the Lord who first loved you.

Put It into Practice!

Beginning Your Budget

The simplest and most effective budget for most young people to use is the **envelope system**. Your "Put It into Practice!" exercise for this lesson is to set up and begin to use the envelope system.

1.) Use one envelope for each spending category.

2.) Label each envelope by spending category.

One would be labeled "giving," another "recreation," and so on.

3.) Label each envelope with the amount you have budgeted for each category.

For example, if you have budgeted $10 a month for recreation, write $10 on the outside of the envelope.

How to use the envelope system

1.) When you receive income, divide the income by placing it in the various envelopes according to the amount you have budgeted for each category.

For instance, you would place $10 in the envelope labeled "recreation."

2.) If you do not receive enough income to fully fund each envelope, put a note in each envelope to remind yourself that it is not fully funded.

For example, if you only place $5 in the recreation envelope, put a note in the envelope reading, "I need $5 more in this account this month."

3.) Do not spend more than you have in any envelope.

For example, if you only have $2 left in the recreation envelope, you can't spend $8 for a recreational activity until more money is deposited into the envelope!

4.) At the end of each month . . .

. . . if there is money left in any envelope, you are free to give it to the Lord, deposit it into your savings account, spend it, or save it for next month.

Chapter 7

Work

Chapter 7 Work

Memorize It!

"Whatever you do, do your work heartily, as for the Lord rather than for men.... It is the Lord Christ whom you serve" (Colossians 3:23-24).

Put It into Practice!

- Complete the "Job Resume" on pages 99-103.

Check It Out!

1.) Read Genesis 39:2-5, Exodus 36:1-2, and Psalm 75:6-7.

What do they tell us about how the Lord is involved in our work?

Genesis 39:2-5

Exodus 36:1-2

Psalm 75:6-7

Do you think most people recognize that the Lord is so involved in their work? Why?

How will understanding God's involvement affect you at work and school?

2.) Read Proverbs 6:6-11, Proverbs 18:9 and 2 Thessalonians 3:7-10.

What do they say about working hard?

Proverbs 6:6-11 —

Proverbs 18:9

2 Thessalonians 3:7-10

Do you work hard? If not, describe what steps you will take to improve your work habits.

Read Exodus 34:21. What does this verse say about rest?

Do you get sufficient rest? If not, how could you increase your rest time?

3.) Read Colossians 3:22-25.

For whom do you really work?

Read 1 Peter 2:18. What does this verse say to you?

How will this understanding change your work habits?

Read Matthew 22:17-21 and Romans 13:1-7. According to these verses, does the Lord require us to pay taxes to the government? Why?

4.) Read the Work Notes on pages 92-98.

What did you find especially interesting?

Do you usually recognize that you are working for the Lord? If not, what will you do to improve this?

*Please write your prayer requests in your **Prayer Log** before coming to class.*

Work

All of us work.

Many have part-time or full-time jobs. Others have school responsibilities. Believe it or not, the average person spends 100,000 hours of his or her life at some sort of work!

For many, this isn't a big deal because they enjoy the work they do—they gain a sense of satisfaction from it. But for others, the only thing they feel about work is frustration.

So what can you do to find enjoyment and satisfaction in your work? The first step is to understand what Scripture teaches about working.

Get It Right

Many of us would like to just forget about work. It would be so much nicer just to have fun all day, every day, right? From the Bible's point of view, that would be a big mistake. When you look through Scripture, you discover that work is important. In Exodus 34:21 God gives this command: *"You shall work six days."* The apostle Paul wrote: *"If anyone will not work, neither let him eat"* (2 Thessalonians 3:10, AMPLIFIED).

Why does work matter so much? One reason is because it develops character. While the carpenter is building a house, the house is also building the carpenter. His skill, diligence and judgment are improved. A student may work at her studies, but her studies also work on her. They refine her thinking processes, broaden her, and teach discipline. A job is not just a task to earn money; it is also intended to produce godly character in the life of the worker. School work is not just something you do to get a passing grade; it also prepares you to deal with life.

All Honest Jobs Are Equally Honorable

As far as God is concerned, one job isn't better than another. There is dignity in all types of work. Scripture does not elevate any honest profession above another. Consider just a few of the wide variety of jobs mentioned in the Scriptures: David was a shepherd and a king; Luke was a doctor; Lydia sold purple fabric; Daniel was a government worker; Paul was a tentmaker; Amos was a fig-picker, and the Lord Jesus was a carpenter. Believe me, if God can use a fig-picker, He can certainly use you in whatever work you do!

> Scripture does not elevate any **honest profession** above another.

God's Part in Work

Just as we needed to understand God's part in handling money, we need to take a look at His part in our work. Scripture reveals that God has three responsibilities when it comes to our work.

God Gives Us Skills

Exodus 36:1 refers to "...*every skillful person in whom the Lord has put skill and understanding to know how to perform all the work.*" God has given each of us special talents. People have different manual skills and intellectual abilities. It is not a matter of one person being better than another; it is simply a matter of having received different abilities from the Creator.

My son Matthew is a terrific surfer. My daughter Danielle is a great piano player. Matt cannot play the piano. God gave them both different talents. Whatever God has given you, use it as well as you possibly can. And remember, your skills are special because they came from God.

God Gives Success

Check out Joseph's life in the Bible. When he was a teen, his brothers tossed him in a well, then sold him as a slave. Joseph went from being his father's favorite son to being a slave. But things got worse when he was thrown into jail for years.

Then suddenly, Joseph was brought before the pharaoh, who was the king, and Joseph became the second most powerful man in all of Egypt! The Bible tells us why: "*The Lord was with Joseph, so he became a successful man.... His master saw that the Lord was with him and how the Lord caused all that he did to prosper in his hand*" (Genesis 39:2-3). It is God who gives us success.

God Controls Promotion

Psalm 75:6-7 reads, "*For promotion and power come from nowhere on earth, but only from God*" (TLB). As much as it may surprise you, your boss is not the one who controls whether or not you will be promoted.

Most people leave God out of their work. They believe that they control their success and their promotions. But leaving God out of work and relying only on themselves is a major reason people experience frustration in their jobs and their studies.

Take a few minutes right now to think about God's part in work. He gives you your skills; He controls success and promotion. What does this mean to you? How will it affect the way you do your work at school or on the job?

Do you want to find joy and satisfaction in your work? Then focus every day on the true source of fulfillment: the Lord.

Our Part in Work

OK, once you understand God's part in your work, the next step is to discover your responsibilities.

Work for the Lord

When you have a job, you're working for your boss, right? WRONG! Scripture reveals we actually are serving the Lord in our work: *"Whatever you do, do your work heartily, as for the Lord rather than for men.... It is the Lord Christ whom you serve"* (Colossians 3:23-24).

Consider your attitude toward work or school. Stop right now and picture Jesus Christ as your boss or teacher. If you were face-to-face with Him, would you try to be more faithful in your job or school work?

If so, then get started. For while you may not be able to see Christ, He is there watching over you, either being pleased or disappointed by how well you are working.

Work Hard

The Scriptures are painfully clear: Hard work is encouraged; laziness is condemned. *"Whatever your hand finds to do, verily, do it with all your might"* (Ecclesiastes 9:10). *"The precious possession of a man is diligence"* (Proverbs 12:27). *"He who is slack in his work is brother to him who destroys"* (Proverbs 18:9).

Paul was one of the most effective workers in the Bible. He endured many tough situations, even beatings and imprisonment. No doubt about it, Paul was a hard worker. *"With labor and hardship we kept working night and day so that we would not be a burden to any of you ... in order to offer ourselves as a model for you, so that you would follow our example"* (2 Thessalonians 3:8-9).

Check out Paul's life in the Bible. You'll find he was an excellent example to all of us regarding hard work.

Don't Overwork!

Working hard must be balanced by the other important things in life. Clearly our first priority is our relationship with the Lord: *"But seek first His kingdom and His righteousness"* (Matthew 6:33).

Rest is important as well. Exodus 34:21 reads, *"You shall work six days, but on the seventh day you shall rest; even during plowing time and harvest you shall rest."* In today's stressful world I believe we need more than ever to apply this principle of resting one day out of seven. This has been difficult for me, particularly when a project is due. Rest can be an issue of faith. Is the Lord able to make our six days of work more productive than seven days? Yes! The Lord gave us this weekly rest for a reason: He knew we would need it to maintain our physical,

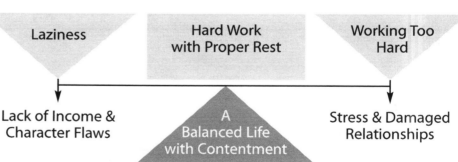

Laziness	Hard Work with Proper Rest	Working Too Hard
Lack of Income & Character Flaws	A Balanced Life with Contentment	Stress & Damaged Relationships

mental, and spiritual health. Study the diagram above to understand the balance God wants in our lives.

Are You A Godly Employee?

When you find a job, you need to do all you can to be a godly employee.

There is a well-known story in the Bible that will help us understand how to be a godly employee: the story of Daniel in the lions' den.

In Daniel chapter 6 we are told that Darius, the king of Babylon, appointed 120 people to lead the government and three men—one of whom was Daniel—to supervise these leaders. The king decided to promote Daniel to govern the entire kingdom. This enraged Daniel's fellow workers. They were jealous and decided to get rid of him. How? By finding some way Daniel had been unfaithful in his job. Unfortunately for them, Daniel was the most faithful employee in the kingdom!

Clearly it was time for Plan B. These schemers suggested to King Darius that it would be a good idea to make a law that everyone in the kingdom must worship only the king or suffer death in the lions' den. Of course, Daniel was faithful to God, so he refused to follow this law. His enemies were thrilled when Daniel continued to worship the one true God. Though the king was upset at having to arrest Daniel, he had no choice. He'd made a law and everyone had to obey. So Daniel was thrown to the lions. But instead of being killed, Daniel survived! God sent an angel to shut the lions' mouths. That next morning, when the king rushed to see if his friend was still alive, he found Daniel waiting to be released, without a scratch on him.

So, what do we learn from this? Six characteristics of a godly employee: Be Honest, Be Faithful, Be a Person of Prayer, Honor Your Employer, Honor Other Employees, and Share Your Faith.

1.) Be Honest

Daniel 6:4 tells us that the workers could find no reason to accuse Daniel in his job, because there was *"no ... evidence of corruption"* in Daniel's work. He was totally honest.

When our son Matthew started a job cleaning offices at night, I counseled him to be totally honest. One night as I was helping him clean, he started to take a piece of candy from a jar on the desk that was there for customers to enjoy. I reminded him of the importance of being honest and never taking even the smallest things without permission. He agreed. Later he asked the boss if he could have a piece of candy while he was cleaning; this small act of honesty really surprised—and impressed—the boss.

2.) Be Faithful

The second characteristic of the godly employee is in Daniel 6:4: *"He was faithful."* Each of us must set a goal of being faithful, of doing our work as excellently as possible. Keep Daniel in mind and do whatever it takes to honor God in your work.

3.) Be a Person of Prayer

The godly employee is a person of prayer. *"Daniel ... continued kneeling on his knees three times a day, praying and giving thanks before his God"* (Daniel 6:10).

Daniel's job was to govern the most powerful country of his day—few of us will ever be faced with his responsibilities and busy schedule—yet he knew the importance of prayer. He never stopped praying, not even when the king commanded him to stop. Daniel knew that prayer is not optional. If you are not praying regularly, you can be sure that your job or school work is suffering.

4.) Honor Your Employer

"Daniel spoke to the king, 'O king, live forever!'" (Daniel 6:21). The king had been forced into

throwing Daniel to the lions, but Daniel's reaction was to honor his boss. Think how natural it would have been to say something like, "You loser! The God who sent His angel to shut the lions' mouths is going to punish you!" Instead, he honored his employer. WOW!

The godly employee always honors his boss. First Peter 2:18 reads, *"Servants [employees], be submissive to your masters [employers] with all respect, not only to those who are good and gentle, but also to those who are unreasonable."*

How do you honor your employer? Never gossip about your boss, even if he's not an ideal person. Do the job you are given as quickly and honestly as possible. Never argue with your boss in front of other employees. Is there something about your employer that you like or respect? Be willing to mention this to others. Are there things he or she does that you think are wrong? Talk to your employer about it when you two are alone. Then leave it to God to show your employer what is best.

Always remember, God ordered us to treat those in authority with respect. If you can't respect the person, respect his or her position. God has put that person in authority for a reason. You may not understand why, but you don't need to. All you need to do is follow God's commands.

And the number one way to honor your employer? Pray for him or her every day. You will benefit from this as much as—if not more than—your employer will!

> A job **well done** earns you the right to tell others that **Jesus is real.**

5.) Honor Other Employees

Relationships on the job aren't always easy. People may try to beat you out of a promotion or even have you fired from your job. Daniel's fellow employees tried to have him killed! Despite this there is no record that Daniel did anything but honor his fellow workers. Never slander another employee behind his back. *"Do not slander a slave [employee] to his master [employer], or he will curse you and you will be found guilty"* (Proverbs 30:10).

6.) Share Your Faith

Daniel shared his faith in God with those around him at the right time. *"The king spoke and said to Daniel, 'Daniel, servant of the living God, has your God, whom you constantly serve, been able to deliver you from the lions?'"* (Daniel 6:20).

King Darius would never have known about the living God if Daniel had not told him. King Darius would not have been influenced by Daniel's sharing his faith in God if he had not seen Daniel's honesty and faithfulness. Because of Daniel's example, Darius's heart was changed: *"I make a decree that . . . men are to fear and tremble before the God of Daniel; for He is the living God and enduring forever, and His kingdom is one which will not be destroyed"* (Daniel 6:26).

Now that's having an affect on someone! Daniel influenced his boss, the king—the most powerful person in the world—to believe in the Lord. You have that same opportunity in your own work or school. Let's say this another way.

A job well done earns you the right to tell others that Jesus is real.

Some Other Work Issues

There are several other work issues that are important for you to know about.

Calling

The Lord has given each of us a special calling or purpose in our lives. Ephesians 2:10 reads, *"For we are His workmanship, created in Christ Jesus for good works, which God prepared beforehand, that we should walk in them."*

Each of us has been created with special physical and mental abilities. You have probably heard the expression, "After the Lord made you, He threw away the mold!" It's true! No one in all of history—past, present, or future—is exactly like you.

Crown has created an awesome tool to help you

discover the career for which He made you. It's called *Career Direct*.® Visit Crown.org to learn more about it.

The Lord created each of us for a particular job, and He gave us the skills and desires to accomplish this work. Your calling may be full-time Christian service or it may be a secular job. Either way, if it's your calling it's right. Don't ever think you aren't serving Christ if you take a secular job. God will use you wherever He wishes! The key is to determine God's call for your life, then respond.

Procrastination

A procrastinator is someone who has a habit of putting things off until later.

Unfortunately, many procrastinate because of laziness or fear.

The opposite of procrastination is a "do it now" attitude. The Bible has many examples of godly people who were prompt. For example—Boaz had the reputation of a person who acted promptly. Look what someone said about him: *"Wait, my daughter, until you know how the matter turns out; for the man will not rest until he has settled it today"* (Ruth 3:18).

Do you struggle with procrastination? You're not alone! Many of us fight with the desire to push a task aside and "do it later." Unfortunately, "later" may never come! Right now, today, you can join the TNT club, whose motto is "Today, Not Tomorrow!"

Here are some suggestions to help you overcome procrastination:

1.) List. List the things you need to do each day.

2.) Prioritize. Decide which tasks you need to accomplish first.

3.) Just Do It. Finish the first task on your list before starting the second. Often that first task is the most difficult or the one you fear the most.

Are You Ready for Taxes?

As you get older you will find that you just can't get away from taxes. Well, you can try. But the people who do so usually end up doing time in jail! Our taxes are based on supply and demand: The government demands and we supply!

As frustrating as this may be at times, we have to honor what the Bible says about taxes. In fact, Jesus Himself responded to a question about whether or not to pay taxes: *"'Is it lawful for us to pay taxes to Caesar, or not?'... [Jesus]* said to them, 'Show Me a denarius [Roman coin]. Whose likeness and inscription does it have?' And they said, 'Caesar's.' And He said to them, 'Then render to Caesar the things that are Caesar's'" (Luke 20:22-25).

In other words, give taxes to the government. This is an example of the contrast between the practices of our society and the teaching of Scripture. Our culture tells us to avoid paying taxes at any cost. But that's not what God says.

Of course, it's okay to reduce your taxes by using legal tax deductions. But the Bible is clear regarding our responsibility to pay taxes! *"Every person is to be in subjection to the governing authorities … for rulers are servants of God, devoting themselves to this very thing. Render to all what is due them: tax to whom tax is due"* (Romans 13:1, 6-7).

You probably don't have to worry about taxes now, but you will. When that day comes, what kind of example will you be for those around you? Will you honor God's guidelines and pay what you owe, without grumbling about the government? Or will you look for every out you can find, even if it's dishonest? Whatever you decide, always remember: The Lord is pleased when you obey Him and pay the taxes you owe.

Retirement

The dictionary defines retirement as "leaving a job, giving up an active life." Too often, that's exactly what happens. Many live their lives waiting for retirement; then, when they reach it, they stop all labor.

Surveys have found that those who become inactive during retirement seldom live for more than a few years. It's as though they lose their reason for living. The Bible teaches that as long as a person is able, he or she should not retire and become unproductive.

Now, just because you "retire" from a job, you don't have to stop working! Age is not a factor in finishing the work the Lord has for you. Moses was 80 years old when he began leading the children of Israel!

Even though it seems far off, start now to plan for your retirement years. Think about what you will want to do when you have more time. Watch for ways you can volunteer and places you can give your abilities, and keep working to accomplish God's plans. Don't stop when you hit 55 or 65. Keep on keeping on with doing the Lord's work.

Summary

Work is a major part of our lives. You work at school, at home, and possibly at a job. Working can be a very positive part of your life, or it can be a terrible drain. But it's up to you to decide which one it is! If you gain God's perspective on work, it will become a blessing.

Put It into Practice!

It is important for you to find the right job. This exercise examines three parts of getting a job: your resume, the letter that accompanies the resume, and preparing for your job interview.

Your Resume

A person seeking a job usually communicates his or her abilities and experience to an employer through a resume. A resume is a brief summary of the education, skills, and experience you can bring to a job.

The resume is often the first impression an employer has of you. For that reason, an attractively designed, well-written resume is important. A resume should be one page in length (never more than two pages). Accuracy and neatness count; so type the resume, making sure it is free of spelling and grammatical errors. Study the sample resume on page 102 and review the directions below before completing your resume.

1.) **Give your name, address, and phone number.**

2.) **State your objective:** Employers like to know what type of position you're interested in.

3.) **Education:** When listing your schools, list the last school first, the number of years you attended and the year you graduated. List any other courses you have taken that may help you do the job.

4.) **Work experience:** Beginning with your last job, list your jobs. For each job list the company's name and address. Give a brief description of your position and the dates you were employed. Note any of your achievements while on the job.

5.) **Other interests/activities:** This section should include school and personal activities or hobbies that might be of interest to an employer. Awards should be included here. Offices held in church, school, or other organizations should be written here as well.

6.) **References:** Be prepared to supply references from other employers or anyone (except family members) who can verify your work abilities and character. You can say, "References furnished upon request" or list at least three people's names, addresses, phone numbers, and job titles. One thing to keep in mind: If you plan to list someone as a reference, be certain to ask that person's permission first. You don't want him or her caught by surprise if your prospective employer calls.

Your Cover Letter

You should send a cover letter with your resume to communicate more personally with the employer. The letter should be done in a businesslike style and should identify the job in which you are interested. It should be brief, and yet explain who you are and why you want the job. It should not exceed one page. Study the sample letter below.

Miss Ima Lookin
123 East Street
Pleasant Town, CA 93001

Mr. Future Employer
CAN-U-HIRE-ME Company
456 Business Avenue
Pleasant Town, CA 93002

Dear Mr. Employer:

I am writing to apply for employment with your company. I have computer and accounting skills that could benefit you. I know your firm employs students who are working their way through college, and I will be attending State University, where I will be studying computer science and accounting. I feel I could be a valuable employee while pursuing my studies.

Attached is a resume that outlines my education, employment experience, and other activities that have enhanced my skills in the area of computers and accounting. References are available upon request.

I hope to interview with you soon. I am available during the day after 1:00 p.m. and have my own transportation.

Thank you for considering my possible employment with your company.

Sincerely yours,

Ima Lookin

Ima Lookin

Enclosures

The Job Interview

Before a company will hire you, usually you will go through a job interview. In fact, you may have to go through several interviews with different people within the company. If you are asked to come for an interview, then you are a candidate for the job. However, just because you are invited to an interview does not mean you are guaranteed the job. It is normal for a company to interview several promising applicants.

There are several things you should do to prepare for the interview:

1.) **Pray.** Ask the Lord to allow you to get the job if He knows it will be one He wants for you. This can be a special time for you to develop a closer walk with Christ.

2.) **Do your homework.** Learn as much about the company as possible before the interview. (Check out their Web site.) What is the business? How is the business conducted? What do they look for in employees? This information will help you demonstrate your understanding of the company during the interview.

3.) **Be careful of your appearance.** Good grooming is a must. Your clothing should be clean and neat. Be careful that you do not dress too casually. Most employers are looking for a conservative and clean-cut look.

4.) **Be on time.** Never arrive late to an interview. Better to arrive 10 minutes early than to arrive one minute late. Remember, the first impression you make is the impression that will last longest in a person's mind.

5.) **Your Resume.** Bring a copy of your resume to the interview in case your resume has been misplaced by the employer.

Job Resume

Name: _Miss Ima Lookin_
Address: _123 East Street_
City/State/Zip: _Pleasant Town, CA 93001_
Phone: _123-555-1234_

Objective: _I am interested in a computer analyst position._

Education: _Outasight High School_
Graduated June 2003
Courses included Computer Basics 101,
Statistics, and Introduction to Calculus.

Work Experience: _High Tech Corporation, 328 West Avenue_
Pleasant Town, CA 93003
Part-time computer programmer during
my senior year. Supervisor—Jesse James
Super Foods Grocery Store, Pleasant Town, CA
Check-out clerk, Summer 1999
Supervisor—Mary Celery

Interests/Activities: _Senior Class Treasurer, Varsity Women's Basketball_
Team, Vice president of Computer Society,
Jogging

References: _Available upon request_

Job Resume

Name: _____
Address: _____
City/State/Zip: _____
Phone: _____

Objective: _____

Education: _____
_____
_____
_____
_____
_____
_____

**Work
Experience:** _____
_____
_____
_____
_____
_____
_____
_____
_____
_____
_____
_____

**Interests/
Activities:** _____
_____
_____
_____
_____

References: _____

Chapter 8

Saving

Chapter **8** Saving

"The wise man saves for the future, but the foolish man spends whatever he gets" (Proverbs 21:20, TLB).

Put It into Practice!

• Complete "Your Savings Account" on page 116.

Check It Out!

1.) Read Genesis 41:34-36, Proverbs 21:20, and Proverbs 30:24-25.

What do these passages say to you about saving?

Genesis 41:34-36

Proverbs 21:20

Proverbs 30:24-25

How will you begin to save if you are not yet saving?

2.) Read Proverbs 21:5, Proverbs 24:27, and Proverbs 27:23-24.

Identify investment principles and share how you can apply them.

Proverbs 21:5	

Proverbs 24:27	

Proverbs 27:23-24	

3.) How would you define gambling?

What are some of the common forms of gambling?

Why do you think people gamble?

Do you think these motives please the Lord? Why or why not?

Read Proverbs 28:20 and Proverbs 28:22. According to these passages, why do you think a godly person should not gamble?

How does gambling violate the scriptural principles of working hard and being a faithful steward of the Lord's possessions?

4.) Read the Saving Notes on pages 110-115.

What proved especially helpful?

Study the principle of compound interest on pages 111-112. Assume you earned 10 percent and saved $20.00 each week (about $1,000 per year). Approximately how much would you accumulate by age 65 if you started saving today? $ _____ (For answer, refer to the graph on page 112.)

*Please write your prayer requests in your **Prayer Log** before coming to class.*

Saving

There's an old saying:

"The secret to financial success is to spend what is left after you save, rather than save what is left after you spend."

Unfortunately, very few people follow these words of wisdom. Not many of us are consistent savers. And that's sad, because the Scriptures encourage us to save.

The Value of Saving

Check out Proverbs 21:20: *"The wise man saves for the future, but the foolish man spends whatever he gets"* (TLB). In Proverbs 30:24-25, an ant is called wise for saving for the future: *"Four things on earth are small, yet they are extremely wise: ants are creatures of little strength, yet they store up their food in the summer"* (NIV).

In Genesis we are told that Joseph saved during the seven years of plenty to survive during the seven years of famine. Joseph understood what saving was all about—not spending all your money today so that you will have something to spend in the future. The biggest reason people don't save is that they are impatient. When they see something they want to buy, they want it now!

Sadly, most people view putting money into savings as a chore, as something that is taking away from them rather than providing for their future.

Now, while you are young, is the best time to discover the value of saving money. If you start this habit now, it will become a natural part of handling money. So how do you develop this habit?

As we discussed already in Chapter 6, the first portion of your income should be given to the Lord. The second should be deposited in your savings account. Think of it this way: If you immediately save a portion of your income each time you are paid, you will save more. Though the Bible does not teach a specific amount or percentage to be saved, we recommend saving at least 10 percent of your income. If you can't do that, don't worry. Begin the habit of saving—even if it's only a dollar a month.

Our daughter, Danielle, worked during the summer and on weekends during school. She did this to save money so she could help buy clothes and pay for extra expenses throughout the year. If she hadn't saved, she wouldn't have had all the things she wanted for school.

We all save for three things:

1.) **For emergencies** — such as an unexpected car repair.
2.) **For future spending** — for buying or replacing items such as clothes, Christmas gifts, a college education, or a car.
3.) **Long-term savings** — for funding long-term needs and goals such as a home purchase or retirement.

Investing—It's Not a Mystery!

People place some of their savings in investments with the hope of receiving an income or growth in value. One quick note: Crown Financial Ministries does not recommend any specific investments. In fact, no one connected with Crown is authorized to use their affiliation to promote the sale of any investments or financial services. What we want to do is simply teach you the scriptural principles for investing.

Principle #1 — Steady Plodding

"Steady plodding brings prosperity; hasty speculation brings poverty" (Proverbs 21:5, TLB). The original Hebrew words for "steady plodding" create the image of a person filling a large barrel with sand one handful at a time. Little by little the barrel is filled to overflowing.

The fundamental principle you need to practice to become a successful investor is to spend less than you earn. Then save and invest the difference over a long period of time.

Examine various investments. Almost all of them are well suited for "steady plodding." A home mortgage is paid off after years of steady payments; savings grow because of compound interest; a business can increase steadily in value over the years.

*Spend less than you earn. Then **save** and **invest** the rest over a long period of time.*

Principle #2 — Compound Interest

Did you notice in that last paragraph what makes your savings grow? Compound interest. This can be your best tool when investing and saving. So what exactly is compound interest? A very wealthy man was once asked if he had seen the seven wonders of the world. He said, "No, but I do know the eighth wonder of the world: compound interest." It's vital that you understand how compounding works.

There are three elements in compounding: the amount you save, the interest rate you earn on your savings, and the length of time you save.

1.) **The amount.** How much you save will be determined by your income and how much you spend. It is our hope that you will be able to increase your saving as you apply God's financial principles.
2.) **The interest rate.** The interest rate is what you earn on an investment. The table on page 112 shows how $1,000 per year grows at various interest rates. As you can see, an increase in the rate of interest has a real impact on the amount accumulated. A two percent increase almost doubles the amount over 40 years. However, be careful not to invest in too risky an investment in order to get a high return. Usually the higher the rate, the higher the risk.

Interest	Year 5	Year 10	Year 20	Year 30	Year 40
6%	5,975	13,972	38,993	83,802	164,048
8%	6,336	15,645	49,423	122,346	279,781
10%	6,716	17,531	63,003	180,943	486,851
12%	7,115	19,665	80,699	270,293	859,142

3.) **Time.** The graph below will help you understand the benefits of starting to save now. If a person faithfully saves $2.74 each day, which is roughly $1,000 per year, and earns 10 percent on the savings, at the end of 50 years the savings will have grown to $1,262,769 and will be earning $10,523 each month in interest alone! Steady plodding pays! However, if the person waits one year before starting, then saves for 49 years, he will accumulate $114,748 less.

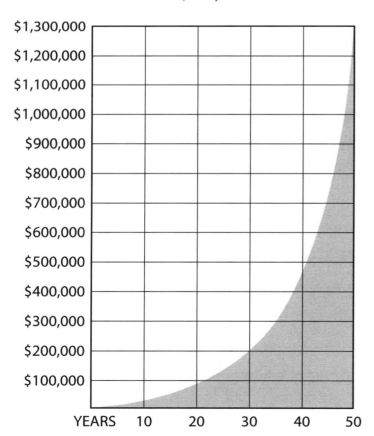

The lesson? Start saving today! To become even more motivated to begin saving now, study the chart on page 113.

Principle #3 — Avoid Risky Investments

"There is another serious problem I have seen everywhere—savings are put into risky investments that turn sour, and soon there is nothing left to pass on to one's son. The man who speculates is soon back to where he began—with nothing" (Ecclesiastes 5:13-15, TLB).

Scripture clearly warns of avoiding risky investments, yet each year thousands of people lose money in high-risk or dishonest investments. How many times have you heard of older people losing their lives' savings on some get-rich-quick scheme? Be sure to pray and seek counsel before you get into any investment.

Other Investment Issues

There are two other issues that are important for you to know about.

Lotteries and Gambling

Lotteries and gambling of all types are sweeping our country. A recent study discovered that people spend 15 times more money on gambling than they donate to churches! The Bible does not specifically prohibit gambling. However, many who gamble do so in an attempt to get rich quick. This is a violation of Scripture.

Sadly, there are millions of people who gamble away their income. Their stories are heartbreaking. In my opinion a godly person should never participate in gambling or lotter-

Question: Who do you think would accumulate more by age 65 ... *Individual A*, who started to save $1,000 a year at age 21, saved for eight years and then completely stopped, or *Individual B*, who saved $1,000 a year for 37 years who started at age 29? Both earned ten percent on their savings. Is it the person who saved a total of $8,000 or the person who saved $37,000? Check it out!

	Individual A			Individual B	
Age	Contribution	Year-End Value		Contribution	Year-End Value
21	1,000	1,100		0	0
22	1,000	2,310		0	0
23	1,000	3,641		0	0
24	1,000	5,105		0	0
25	1,000	6,716		0	0
26	1,000	8,487		0	0
27	1,000	10,436		0	0
28	1,000	12,579		0	0
29	0	13,837		1,000	1,100
30	0	15,221		1,000	2,310
31	0	16,743		1,000	3,641
32	0	18,417		1,000	5,105
33	0	20,259		1,000	6,716
34	0	22,284		1,000	8,487
35	0	24,513		1,000	10,436
36	0	26,964		1,000	12,579
37	0	29,661		1,000	14,937
38	0	32,627		1,000	17,531
39	0	35,889		1000	20,384
40	0	39,478		1,000	23,523
41	0	43,426		1,000	26,975
42	0	47,769		1,000	30,772
43	0	52,546		1,000	34,950
44	0	57,800		1,000	39,545
45	0	63,580		1,000	44,599
46	0	69,938		1,000	50,159
47	0	76,932		1,000	56,275
48	0	84,625		1,000	63,003
49	0	93,088		1,000	70,403
50	0	103,397		1,000	78,543
51	0	112,636		1,000	87,497
52	0	123,898		1,000	97,347
53	0	136,290		1,000	108,182
54	0	149,919		1,000	120,100
55	0	164,911		1,000	133,210
56	0	181,402		1,000	147,631
57	0	199,542		1,000	163,494
58	0	219,496		1,000	180,943
59	0	241,466		1,000	200,138
60	0	265,590		1,000	221,252
61	0	292,149		1,000	244,477
62	0	321,364		1,000	270,024
63	0	353,501		1,000	298,127
64	0	388,851		1,000	329,039
65	0	427,736		1,000	363,043

Total Investment $8,000

Total Investment $37,000

Total Amount Accumulated $427,736

Total Amount Accumulated $363,043

ies—even for entertainment. We should not expose ourselves to the risk of becoming compulsive gamblers, nor should we support an industry that enslaves so many.

I pray that you will make the commitment never to gamble a penny.

Wills

A will is a document that determines who will receive your money and possessions after you die. In the Bible, Isaiah told Hezekiah, *"Thus says the Lord, 'Set your house in order, for you shall die'"* (2 Kings 20:1).

Someday we all will die. We all will. One of the greatest gifts you can leave your family for that emotional time will be a properly prepared will or trust. It's probably early for you to do so right now, but don't let it go until it's too late.

The Only Guaranteed Investment

I was 28 years old when I found the only guaranteed investment that exists. I started meeting weekly with several young men and was impressed by their lives. At that time I was part owner of a successful restaurant, had married my wonderful wife, Bev, and we lived in a nice home. I had everything I thought would make me happy, but something was missing.

I was surprised to hear that these men really believed in God. I did not have what they had—a personal relationship with Jesus Christ. A friend described how I could have a relationship with the Lord. He told me about five things that I had never understood before.

God Loves You and Wants You to Know Him

"For God so loved the world, that He gave His only begotten Son, that whoever believes in Him shall not perish, but have eternal life" (John 3:16). When my son Matthew was in the first grade he really wanted to win the 100-yard dash at his school's field day. That was all we heard about for two months. But there was a problem: His classmate, Bobby, was faster than he was.

Field day finally arrived. They ran the 50-yard dash first, and Bobby beat Matthew badly. I will never forget when Matthew came up to me with tears in his eyes and said, "Daddy, please pray for me in the 100-yard dash. I've just got to win." My heart sank as I nodded.

With the sound of the gun, Matthew got off to a quick start. Halfway through the race he pulled away from the rest of his classmates and won. I lost control of myself! I was jumping and shouting! And then I understood how much I loved my son. Although I love other people, I do not love them enough to give my son to die for them. But that is how much God the Father loved you. He gave His only Son, Jesus Christ, to die for you.

Unfortunately, We Are Separated from God

God is holy—which means He is perfect—and He cannot have a relationship with anyone who is not also perfect. Every person has sinned and is separated from God.

"For all have sinned and fall short of the glory of God" (Romans 3:23). This diagram illustrates our separation from God:

PEOPLE (Sinful)   **GOD** (Holy)

A gap separates people from God. They try without success to bridge this gap through their own efforts, such as living a good life.

God's Only Provision for the Gap Is Jesus Christ

Jesus Christ died on the cross to pay the penalty for our sin and bridge the gap from people to God.

"Jesus said to him, 'I am the way, and the truth, and the life; no one comes to the Father, but through Me'" (John 14:6). *"But God demonstrates His own love toward us, in that while we were yet sinners, Christ died for us"* (Romans 5:8).

This diagram illustrates our union with God through Jesus Christ:

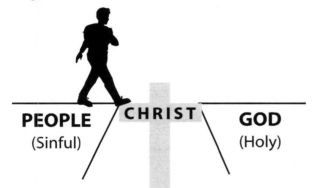

PEOPLE CHRIST **GOD**
(Sinful)   (Holy)

This Relationship Is a Gift From God

My friend went on to explain that I could receive the relationship with God as a free gift. *"For by grace you have been saved through faith; and that not of yourselves, it is the gift of God; not as a result of works, that no one may boast"* (Ephesians 2:8-9).

We Must Each Receive Jesus Christ

I had to ask Jesus Christ to come into my life and become my Savior and Lord. And I did it! I am a very practical person. If something does not work, I stop it quickly. I can tell you from 30 years' experience that a relationship with God is available to you through Jesus Christ. Knowing Jesus is the greatest experience in life!

If you want to know the Lord and are not sure if you do, I encourage you to receive Christ right now. Pray a prayer like this: "Lord, I need You. I invite Jesus to come into my life as my Savior and Lord and to make me the person You want me to be. Thank You for forgiving my sins and giving me the gift of eternal life."

If you have just asked Christ into your life, welcome to the family of God! You've taken the most important step you will ever take. Now, please tell your leader so he or she will be able to help you in your spiritual growth.

Summary

It's vitally important to start saving early. You can do that in many different ways, including through investments. But the most important investment you will ever make is that of accepting God's offer of eternal life through Jesus Christ.

"THIS IS A FREE GIFT FROM GOD!"

Put It into Practice!

The "Put It into Practice!" exercise for this chapter is to open your savings account, if you do not already have one, and to establish your savings goals.

Open Your Savings Account

Contact different financial institutions (banks, credit unions, or stock brokers) to determine the following:

> 3   **What is the minimum amount needed to open a savings account?**
>
> 3   **Are there any fees they charge for the account?**
>
> 3   **What rate of interest do they pay on the money you have deposited?**
>
> 3   **Are the deposits insured?**
>
> 3   **What should you bring when you open the savings account (items such as personal identification, your social security number, etc.)?**

Establish Your Savings Goals

After you have opened your account, establish the habit of regularly depositing a certain amount of savings into the account—**and watch the balance in your account increase as it compounds!**

Sample Savings Goals:
1. *Save to buy a used car for cash.*
2. *Save to buy another surfboard.*
3. *Save for college.*

My Savings Goals:

Chapter **9**

Friends

Chapter 9 Friends

Memorize It!

"Let no one look down on your youthfulness, but rather in speech, conduct, love, faith and purity, show yourself an example of those who believe" (1 Timothy 4:12).

Put It into Practice!

- Complete "Your Financial Goals" on pages 127-129.

Check It Out!

1.) According to 1 Corinthians 15:33, do our friends influence us?

Why is it important to have a godly group of friends?

Read 1 Timothy 4:12. What does this verse say about how young people should be an example?

Describe some ways you can be an example and influence others to handle money in a way that will please the Lord.

Define partiality:

2.) Read Leviticus 19:15, Deuteronomy 10:17 and James 2:1-9.

What does Scripture say about partiality (showing favoritism)?

> Leviticus 19:15

> Deuteronomy 10:17

> James 2:1-9

Do you tend to favor the friendship of those who are rich or popular over others? Why or why not?

If you believe you are partial, read Romans 12:16 and Philippians 2:3. What guidance do these verses give you to overcome partiality?

> Romans 12:16

> Philippians 2:3

3.) Read 1 Corinthians 3:16-17.

If you have invited Jesus Christ into your life, where does God dwell?

Since your body is a temple that God lives in, how should you care for yourself physically?

Do you eat nutritious food and get enough exercise and sleep? If not, why?

4.) Read the Friends Notes on pages 122-126.

What did you find most interesting in this section?

How will what you learned impact your life?

*Please write your prayer requests in your **Prayer Log** before coming to class.*

Friends

Mike was raised in a loving family who knew the Lord.

He was a good student and a great basketball player. When Mike reached 13, a new boy moved into the neighborhood.

The new kid did not know God and did many things Mike had been taught not to do. Still, they had some things in common, and so they became close friends.

Before long Mike was listening to music that promoted murder. Then his new friend introduced him to drugs. The effect of this was radical: Mike quit the basketball team and then dropped out of school. He started hanging out with kids who were selling drugs and who weren't interested in knowing Jesus. His new friends almost destroyed him.

Today Mike is 22 years old and is still struggling in his relationship with the Lord and with getting direction for his life.

Scripture teaches that we are influenced, either for good or evil, by our friends. Paul wrote, *"Do not be deceived: Bad company corrupts good morals'"* (1 Corinthians 15:33). Read this verse again. "Do not be deceived: bad company corrupts good morals." Let this sink in. We should be very careful about who we choose for our closest friends.

"I MUST BE THE SALT OF THE WORLD."

Answer these questions:
1.) Have I asked the Lord to give me close Christian friends?
2.) Do my best friends encourage me in my walk with Christ?
3.) How would I describe my closest friends?

Our best friends should know the Lord. However, the Lord doesn't want us to avoid everyone who does not know Him. No way! In fact, we are to be salt and light!

Are You Salty Enough?

Ever tried to eat french fries when they don't have enough salt on them? Kind of like chewing a mushy stick, isn't it? Tasteless. Salt is an important part of our diet. It adds flavor, spice, and fun to our food. In the Old West, salt was one of the most valued items a person could have, not just because it flavored things but because it preserved them! Salt kept meat good for a long time, which meant pioneers could store food to eat later without worrying about it spoiling.

In Matthew 5:13, Jesus discusses the importance of salt. He says, *"You are the salt of the earth. But if the salt has become tasteless, how can it be made salty again? It is no longer good for anything, except to be thrown out."* Jesus knew salt had to be strong—salty—to be of any use.

Anyone who is a believer is "salt" to the people around him or her. They should be an example of God's truth. When you accept Christ as your Savior, you are actually entering into a kind of contract with God. You are saying, "OK, I believe in You, and I want You to be in control of my life." And God says, "Great! Now I can teach you—and I can use you to show all those people around you how great it is to follow Me."

Believe it or not, people are watching you. "Not me. I'm too young!" you say? Yes, you! First Timothy 4:12 says it this way: *"Let no one look down on your youthfulness, but rather in speech, conduct, love, faith and purity, show yourself an example of those who believe."* There are people around you all the time, and they are watching you, just as they watch anyone who claims to be following God. This is especially true when it comes to handling money. You are a reflection of God's truth. When you handle money God's way, you are showing others that it can be done. And when God honors your obedience, those people who are watching will be affected. And they may even decide that Christ is real!

So how do you go about being an example?

By What You Say

There's an old saying that goes something like this, "It's OK if your feet slip, but when your tongue slips—disaster follows!" The tongue is such a small part of the body, and yet it has incredible power! Check out what James says

about the tongue in James 3:5-6: *"Consider what a great forest is set on fire by a small spark. The tongue also is a fire, a world of evil among the parts of the body. It corrupts the whole person, sets the whole course of his life on fire, and is itself set on fire by hell"* (NIV). Now that's powerful!

When you talk about the way you handle money, what kind of impression are you giving? Do you moan and complain about never having as much as you want and about having to give to God? Do you talk about what you would do if you were rich? Or are you thankful for the many blessings God has given you, and the ways in which God has helped you?

Every time you open your mouth, you are either being a light or you are adding to the darkness. You are either being salt or starting a fire. What kind of example are you being with your words?

By What You Do

Remember the saying "What you're doing speaks so loudly I can't hear what you're saying"? Paul understood this principle. In 1 Corinthians 11:1, he says, *"Be imitators of me, just as I also am of Christ."* If you learn nothing else, learn this: People may doubt what you say, but they almost always believe what you do!

Do you talk a good game about following God's direction with money but fail to carry through in your actions? Do you practice what you preach, or is it just lip service? Too many

have failed to live what they say they believe, proving to a skeptical world that godly talk doesn't mean a godly walk. When you say one thing and do another, people aren't just judging you, they are judging the Lord, as well. After all, you're the example of who God is.

Ask God to help you be faithful with both your mouth and your actions. Pray that He will show you how to make your words and your actions honor Him. He's listening, and He will answer.

Beware of Partiality

Read carefully James 2:1-6, 8-9: *"Do not hold your faith in our glorious Lord Jesus Christ with an attitude of personal favoritism. For if a man comes into your assembly with a gold ring and dressed in fine clothes, and there also comes in a poor man in dirty clothes, and you pay special attention to the one who is wearing the fine clothes, and say, 'You sit here in a good place,' and you say to the poor man, 'You stand over there, or sit down by my footstool'; have you not made distinctions among yourselves, and become judges with evil motives?*

Listen, my beloved brethren: did not God choose the poor of this world to be rich in faith and heirs of the kingdom which He promised to those who love Him? But you have dishonored the poor man.... If, however, you are fulfilling the royal law, according to the Scripture, 'You shall love your neighbor as yourself,' you are doing well. But if you show partiality, you are committing sin and are convicted by the law as transgressors."

I have struggled with the sin of partiality. I would not be so obvious as to tell one to stand and another to sit in a good place, but in my heart I have been guilty of favoritism, and this has influenced my actions. Once, when I hung up the phone, my wife said, "I know you weren't talking to Ken; it must have been Stan. You like Ken better, and it shows in your voice."

Partiality does not have to be based on a person's wealth. It can also be based on a person's status at school or his or her appearance. James 2:9 could not be more direct: *"But if you show partiality, you are committing sin and are convicted by the law as transgressors."* How do we break the habit of partiality?

Romans 12:10 tells us, *"Be devoted to one another in brotherly love; give preference to one another in honor."* And Philippians 2:3 reads, *"With humility of mind regard one another as more important than yourselves."* Ask the Lord to help you with the habit of thinking of each person, regardless of who it is, as more important than yourself.

One way to overcome partiality is to concentrate on the abilities of each person. Every person can do some things better than we can. Keeping this in mind and looking for it will help you learn to appreciate all people—and it will make you a much more effective example of God's way of living.

Maintain Your Temple

Why should we take good care of our bodies? And what does this have to do with money? Those are good questions and there are good answers.

When people ask Jesus Christ to become their Savior, the Spirit of God comes in to live in their bodies. They actually become temples of God. First Corinthians 3:16-17 says it this way: *"Do you know that you are a temple of God and that the Spirit of God dwells in you? If any man destroys the temple of God, God will destroy him, for the temple of God is holy, and that is what you are."* Pretty strong words from the Lord.

You might think, "I'd never destroy my body!" But many of us are doing just that through poor sleeping and eating habits, lack of exercise (the "couch potato syndrome"), drinking alcohol, and using tobacco or drugs.

Taking care of yourself may not rank high in your prioritiy list. We like to think we'll live forever, that nothing can hurt us. But we can't get away with mistreating our bodies. Consider the following ways to take care of your health.

Nutrition

What would happen if you put molasses in a car's gas tank instead of gasoline? Think it would run? Definitely not! You'd be replacing an engine in no time! Well, your body is similar. You need the right fuel to keep it running well.

Surfing the **Internet** or **TV** channels is not considered **exercise!**

Many people have diets that are too high in sugars and fats. For example, did you know that there are 12 teaspoons of sugar in one soft drink, and that most have as much caffeine as a cup of coffee? Too much sugar contributes to disease. Caffeine can make you hyper, unable to focus, and also affects your sleep.

Good nutrition consists of the proper balance of protein, vegetables, fruits, and complex carbohydrates—not a steady diet of junk food.

Exercise

Regular exercise is the second important ingredient in maintaining good health. Surfing the Internet or TV channels is not considered exercise! Neither is jogging to the refrigerator and back during a TV commercial. Three times a week you need vigorous exercise. It need not be boring. Experiment to find the type of exercise you really enjoy doing. You can swim; play basketball, soccer, baseball, or volleyball; jog, hike, or walk; ride bikes; surf, boogie board, or water-ski; lift weights; or whatever you enjoy doing. Exercise can be fun.

Sleep

The third way to maintain a healthy body is to get enough sleep. This does not mean sleeping through math or chemistry class! A recent study found most teens were not getting adequate sleep. The amount of sleep one needs varies from person to person. However, most people function best on seven to eight hours of sleep a night.

Tobacco, Alcohol and Drugs

You've heard it a million times: Just Say No! And say it to all three of these body destroyers. Not one is good for you—most of them could kill you. Smoking has been linked to cancer, and it causes early aging of the skin. In other words, wrinkles!

Drinking alcohol can rob a person of his or her money, career, family, and health. The number of people killed by drunk drivers is mind-boggling.

An epidemic of drug use has invaded our country. Drugs can destroy the body, mind, and wallet. All of us know of teens who have died from drug use and left behind grieving families and friends. Many crimes are committed because people will steal or kill to get money to buy drugs.

Some teens face a lot of peer pressure to do drugs. But remember what 2 Corinthians 6:16 says, *"We are the temple of the living God; just as God said, 'I will dwell in them and walk among them; and I will be their God, and they shall be My people.'"*

God lives in you. He doesn't want you to ruin your body and mind by doing drugs.

It Pays to Stay Healthy!

If the average person saved the money he or she spent on junk food and other habits that are not healthy, they would be surprised at the amount of money they could save. Why don't you try it? You might be surprised too!

Summary

Remember to choose your close friends very carefully. Ask the Lord to bring friends into your life that will help you grow closer to Him. Learning how to handle money God's way is something that will not only benefit us, but it can benefit others as they see our example. We can give those around us a peek into the peace and joy of a relationship with the Lord. So watch your words and actions and be sure you have surrendered them to the One who longs to use you, as salt and light, to bless others around you.

> Remember to choose your close **friends** very carefully.

Put It into Practice!

Your Financial Goals

Writing down your financial goals will help you plan to accomplish what is really important to you. Here's how to start:

1.) **Complete the Financial Goals worksheet (page 129).**

2.) **Pray for the Lord to confirm your goals.** Do not limit your goals by looking only at where you are now. Remember that God has a part and so do you. Our part is to do what we can. Some of your goals may be "faith goals" that you must trust the Lord to provide.

3.) **Prioritize your goals.** For instance, funding your education might be more important than buying an entertainment center. You don't have to accomplish all your goals at once. For example, your budget may not allow you to save for an entertainment center until you buy your school clothes.

4.) **List your goals for the coming year.**

Financial Goals

Income Goals: The amount of income I would like to earn this year $ _2,000_

Giving Goals: I would like to give _10_ % of my income to _my church_

Other Giving Goals: _Give to missionary, Mr. Harris_

Savings and Investment Goals: I would like to save _20_ % of my income.

Other Saving Goals: _Save for car, surfboard, and college_

I would like to make the following investments: _____

Educational Goals: I would like to fund the following education.

School: _Help toward college_

Major Purchase Goals: I would like to make the following major purchase(s) (car, etc.)

Item	Amount
Car	_$3,500_

Other Financial Goals: _____

Goals For This Year:

I believe the Lord wants me to achieve the following goals this year:

Priority	Financial Goals	My Part	God's Part
1	_Save 20%_	_Spend wisely_	_Help my spending_
2	_Earn $2,000_	_Look for job_	_Provide job_
3			

Financial Goals

Income Goals: The amount of income I would like to earn this year $ _____

Giving Goals: I would like to give _____ % of my income to _____

Other Giving Goals: _____

_____

Savings and Investment Goals: I would like to save _____ % of my income.

Other Saving Goals: _____

_____

I would like to make the following investments: _____

_____

Educational Goals: I would like to fund the following education.

School: _____

_____

Major Purchase Goals: I would like to make the following major purchase(s) (car, etc.)

Item	Amount
_____	_____
_____	_____
_____	_____

Other Financial Goals: _____

_____

_____

_____

Goals For This Year:

I believe the Lord wants me to achieve the following goals this year:

Priority	Financial Goals	My Part	God's Part
1	_____	_____	_____
2	_____	_____	_____
3	_____	_____	_____

Chapter 10

Go For It!

Chapter 10

Go For It!

Memorize It!

"I have learned to be content in whatever circumstances I am. I know how to get along with humble means, and I also know how to live in prosperity.... I can do all things through Him who strengthens me" (Philippians 4:11-13).

Put It into Practice!

- Complete "Insurance Needs" on page 141.
- Complete "Your Financial Statement" on pages 142-144.

Check It Out!

1.) How would you define contentment?

What do Philippians 4:11-13, 1 Timothy 6:6-8, and Hebrews 13:5-6 have to say about contentment?

Philippians 4:11-13

1 Timothy 6:6-8

Hebrews 13:5-6

How does our culture discourage contentment?

2.) Complete the Insurance Needs exercise on page 141.

Look up the word "prosperity" in the dictionary. What does it mean?

3.) Read Joshua 1:8 and Hebrews 11:36-40.

What do these passages say to you about financial prosperity for the believer?

Joshua 1:8

Hebrews 11:36-40

Think about the lives of Job, Joseph, King David, and Paul. Check out their stories in the Bible. Describe how they experienced times of plenty and times when there wasn't a lot of money.

Is financial prosperity something all Christians should always experience? Why or why not?

Describe the lifestyle you would like to have when you grow up (what kind of home, transportation, clothes, giving, vacations, etc.).

Estimate how much these will cost each month and how much you'll need to earn.

How do you plan on accomplishing this?

4.) Read the Go for It! Notes on pages 136-140.

What concept interested you most in the Notes?

Describe any spending habits you sense the Lord wants you to change.

Thinking of the entire study, what was the most helpful part for you?

*Please write your prayer requests in your **Prayer Log** before coming to class.*

Go For It!

First Timothy 6:8 says,

"If we have food and covering, with these we shall be content." **Look at this passage again.**

It says that if you have food and covering (clothes and shelter), you should be content. Our culture would say something like this: "If you can afford the finest food, wear the latest fashions, drive the newest sports car, and live in a beautiful home, then you can be happy." It assumes that happiness means having more things.

The word "contentment" is mentioned seven times in Scripture, and six times it has to do with money. Paul wrote, *"I have learned to be content in whatever circumstances I am. I know how to get along with humble means, and I also know how to live in prosperity; in any and every circumstance I have learned the secret of being filled and going hungry, both of having abundance and suffering need. I can do all things through Him who strengthens me"* (Philippians 4:11-13).

Review this passage. Paul "learned" to be content. We are not born content—no way. But we can learn contentment. Here's how.

Know what God wants of you; do what God wants; trust God to do His part.

It is not just knowing these things that brings contentment; it is doing them.

Be faithful. Then you can be content knowing the Lord will give you exactly what will be best for you at this time. But remember, being content involves doing something. Don't mistake contentment with laziness. Because we serve the living and awesome God, Christians should always be improving. Contentment is an inner peace that accepts what God has chosen for us in our current work, school, and finances. Hebrews 13:5 tells us to continue *"being content with what you have; for He Himself has said, 'I will never desert you, nor will I ever forsake you.'"*

Living a Contented Life

The Bible does not promise the same lifestyle for everyone. In Scripture godly people are in all walks of life, rich and poor. But whatever your circumstances, you can live in such a way that you find contentment. Here are several principles that will help you do this.

1.) Keep thinking about eternity.

When you're young, it's hard to believe you'll ever die—but we all will. To understand how brief life is on earth, picture life as follows:

KNOWING what God requires of us in handling money and possessions	**+**	**DOING** those requirements	**+**	**TRUSTING** God to provide exactly what He knows is best	**=**	**CONTENTMENT**

Our short time on earth is but a dot on the time line of eternity, yet we have the opportunity to impact eternity by how we handle money today. Not only can we lay up treasures for ourselves in heaven, but we are able to spend money in such a way that we can influence people for Jesus Christ.

As you decide how to spend your money, ask yourself this question: "What will have the most impact in light of eternity?"

Moses is a good example of this. Check out Hebrews 11:24-26: *"By faith Moses, when he had grown up, refused to be called the son of Pharaoh's daughter; choosing rather to endure ill-treatment with the people of God than to enjoy the passing pleasures of sin; considering the reproach of Christ greater riches than the treasures of Egypt; for he was looking to the reward."*

Moses faced a choice. As Pharaoh's adopted son he could enjoy the riches of royalty, or he could choose to become a Hebrew slave. Because he had an eternal perspective, he chose to become a slave and was used by the Lord in a wonderful way. We face a similar decision. We can either live with a view toward eternity or focus on this present world.

Have you ever returned to a place you knew as a young child? I once visited a field on which I had played when I was six years old. I remembered it as a huge field surrounded by towering fences. I was shocked to discover how small it really was! Or do you remember how at one time you wanted to buy something so badly that you thought you couldn't live another minute without it? Yet today it means almost nothing to you!

I think we will experience a similar feeling when we arrive in heaven. Many things that seem so large and important to us now will seem so unimportant then. Don't let the "here and now" make you forget that there is eternity waiting!

2.) Don't give in to the comparison game.

There is only one Person to whom we should be comparing ourselves: Jesus Christ. Don't waste your time worrying that you're not as rich or as handsome or as ANYTHING as someone else. None of that matters. All that counts for eternity is how closely you are following the Lord.

Comparing ourselves to others robs us of joy and contentment, and it often prompts us to spend unwisely.

3.) Freely enjoy whatever you spend in the "Spirit."

Prayerfully submit your spending decisions to the Lord. Everything you have is owned by the Lord, right? Right. So spend to please Him and not for a selfish purpose. And don't worry.

Just because you are seeking the Lord's direction in your spending does not mean that you'll never get to spend for fun! God loves to give His children gifts and to delight them.

If you turn your spending over to Him, you'll find more fun and enjoyment than you ever dreamed possible. And you won't regret any of it the next day. *"For everything created by God is good, and nothing is to be rejected if it is received with gratitude"* (1 Timothy 4:4).

4.) Apart from Christ, wealth is meaningless.

Leslie Flynn, in his book *Your God and Your Gold*, pointed out: "Solomon had an annual income of more than $25 million. He lived in a palace that took 13 years to build. He owned 40,000 stalls of horses. He sat on an ivory throne overlaid with gold. He drank from gold cups."

Solomon knew whether or not money would bring true happiness! His conclusion? Check out Ecclesiastes 12:8: *"Vanity of vanities … all is vanity!"* It was worthless! All the wealth in the world, and it didn't do him any good. Nothing can replace the value of our relationship with the Lord. *"For what does it profit a man to gain the whole world, and forfeit his soul?"* (Mark 8:36). What good? None at all!

5.) Don't go along with the world.

Romans 12:2 begins with this command, *"Do not be conformed to this world."*

Advertisers stress the importance of image rather than function. For example, automobile ads rarely focus on a car as reliable transportation. Instead, an image of status or sex appeal is communicated.

Think about the claims of TV commercials. No matter what the product—clothing, deodorants, credit cards, cars, beverages, and so on—advertisers want you to believe that all you have to do is buy their product and you will suddenly be attractive, happy, and living the "good life."

From time to time we all get hooked on something we think we must buy: car, sound system, camera, boat—you name it. Once hooked, it's very easy to talk yourself into purchasing anything. Remember to seek the Lord's direction and the counsel of a godly person when making a spending decision.

6.) Don't let television, video gaming, or the 'Net get to you.

Television, gaming, and the Internet have affected us in many ways. Consider this: By the time the average teen graduates from high school, he has spent 10,800 hours in class and 15,000 hours in front of the "tube." The average American child spends more time watching television (30 to 50 hours per week) than in any other activity except sleeping—and he will see about one million commercials by age 20. And guess what those ads want you to do? Spend money on their stuff! Be careful of the tube—it could cost you money.

Poverty, Prosperity, or Stewardship?

We all want to have enough money to take care of our needs, but when it comes to wealth, some Christians are extreme. The first extreme is believing that you must be poor because a wealthy person cannot have a close relationship with Christ. The second extreme is the belief that any Christian walking by faith will always be rich.

In the Old Testament the Lord rewarded the children of Israel with prosperity when they were obedient, while poverty was one of the results of disobedience. Deuteronomy 30:15-16 reads, *"I have set before you today life and prosperity, and death and adversity; in that I command you today to love the Lord your God, to walk in His ways and to keep His commandments … that the Lord your God may bless you."*

Moreover, Psalm 35:27 reads, *"The Lord … delights in the prosperity of His servant."* It's fine to pray for prosperity when our relationship with the Lord is healthy. *"Beloved, I pray that in all respects you may prosper and be in good health, just as your soul prospers"* (3 John 2).

The Bible does not teach that a godly person must live in poverty. However, some others believe that all godly people will always be rich if they just have enough faith. This extreme is not true either.

prosperity and poverty. He was born into a prosperous family, then was thrown into a pit and sold into slavery by his brothers. While Joseph was a slave, his master, Potiphar, promoted him to be head of his household. Later he made the right decision not to commit adultery with Potiphar's wife, yet was thrown in jail because of that decision. In God's timing he was finally elevated to Prime Minister of Egypt.

The guideline for prosperity is found in Joshua 1:8. Read this slowly: *"This book of the law shall not depart from your mouth, but you shall meditate on it day and night, so that you may be careful to do according to all that is written in it; for then you will make your way prosperous, and then you will have success."*

There are two requirements for prosperity in this passage: regular meditation on the Scriptures and doing all that is written in them. Once you have done this, you place yourself in the position to be blessed financially, but there's no guarantee that the godly will always prosper.

	Poverty	Stewardship	Prosperity
Possessions are	Evil	A responsibility	A right
I work to	Meet only basic needs	Serve Christ	Become rich
Godly people are	Poor	Faithful	Wealthy
Ungodly people are	Wealthy	Unfaithful	Poor
I give	Because I must	Because I love God	To get
My spending is	Without gratitude to God	Prayerful and responsible	Carefree and consumptive

Will Godly People Always Prosper?

Look at the life of Joseph. He's a good example of a faithful person who experienced

Why Do the Wicked Prosper?

This is a question God's people have asked for centuries. The prophet Jeremiah asked, *"Why does the way of the wicked prosper?"* (Jeremiah 12:1, NIV).

The psalmist also asked why the wicked prospered, and he admitted being envious of them. Godliness did not seem to "pay off." Then the Lord revealed the wicked person's end: eternal punishment. *"I envied the arrogant when I saw the prosperity of the wicked ... then I understood their final destiny. Surely you place them on slippery ground; you cast them down to ruin. How suddenly are they destroyed, completely swept away by terrors!"* (Psalm 73:3, 17-19, NIV).

The Bible tells us that some of the wicked will prosper, but it does not tell us why. What we're told is not to worry. Don't envy the wicked person who prospers, because life on earth is so short. *"Do not fret because of evil men or be envious of those who do wrong; for like the grass they will soon wither, like green plants they will soon die away"* (Psalm 37:1-2, NIV).

Summary

At the very beginning of this book we asked why the Bible said so much about money, why it mentioned money in more than 2,350 verses. There are three major reasons:

1.) **How we handle money impacts our fellowship with the Lord;**
2.) **Money is the primary competitor with Christ for our love; and**
3.) **The way we handle money molds our character.**

In addition, the Lord recognized how important money issues would be to us, His children, so He gave us a blueprint for handling money His way.

So where do you go now? It's simple: Your job is to make a real effort to be faithful, no matter how small it may appear, and then leave

the results to God. I love what the Lord said to the prophet Zechariah, *"Who has despised the day of small things?"* (Zechariah 4:10). Don't be discouraged. Be faithful in even the smallest matters. You've taken a step forward by discovering God's way of handling money, but now you must act upon it. Jesus said, *"Everyone who hears these words of Mine and acts upon them, may be compared to a wise man who built his house on the rock. And the rain fell, and the floods came, and the winds blew and slammed against that house; and yet it did not fall, for it had been founded on the rock"* (Matthew 7:24-25).

We appreciate the time you have invested in this study. We pray it has given you a greater appreciation for the Scriptures, and, above all else, nurtured your love for Jesus Christ. Your relationship with Him is the greatest treasure of all. May He continue to guide and lead you as you seek to serve Him.

Put It into Practice!

Insurance Needs

As you grow older and take on added responsibilities, such as a job or car, it will become necessary for you to consider insurance. The purpose of insurance is to reduce the risk of loss.

The amount and type of insurance you carry will be determined by your needs and budget. Because insurance can be difficult to understand, seek experienced counsel when making your insurance decisions.

The section below contains a brief explanation of six common types of insurance and a short exercise for you to complete.

> 3 **Automobile Insurance.** Most states require that insurance be carried by car owners. Automobile insurance includes several kinds of coverage for different losses that you might experience.
>
> 3 **Health or Medical Insurance.** Health insurance pays for doctor, hospital, and other health-related expenses. The cost of health care, particularly if there is a major illness, can be very expensive.
>
> 3 **Homeowners or Renters Insurance.** Homeowners or renters insurance covers property, such as furniture, clothing, and a home. You should make a list of all your property and keep it somewhere other than your house or apartment in case you suffer loss.
>
> 3 **Life Insurance.** The purpose of life insurance is to provide money to the survivors should a person die.
>
> 3 **Liability Insurance.** Liability insurance protects you in case someone sues you.
>
> 3 **Disability Insurance.** Disability pays you an income if you cannot work due to an injury or illness.

Please complete the following:

1.) Describe any insurance needs you currently have or will have in the near future:

_____

2.) What steps will you take to get this insurance?

_____

3.) Who will serve as your insurance counselor?_____

Your Financial Statement

A financial statement is used to help a person get a picture of his or her current financial situation. It's not necessary to be exact to the penny; rather, estimate the value of each asset (what you own) and the amount of each liability (what you owe). A sample of a financial statement is found on the next page, and a form for you to complete is on page 144.

We recommend that you update your financial statement once each year to help you keep up with your progress. I update my financial statement around January 1 of each year. Please remember to use a pencil so you can make changes easily.

Your Financial Statement

ASSETS (what you own) **Date** *January 10*

Cash and checking account	50.00
Savings	625.00
Stocks and bonds	0
Coins	50.00
Car	0
Furniture/Electronics	100.00
Jewelry	25.00
Other personal items	0
Other assets	0
TOTAL ASSETS:	**850.00**

LIABILITIES (what you owe)

Current bills	15.00
Credit card debt	0
Car loan	0
Personal debts to relatives	50.00
Educational loans	0
Bank loans	0
Other debts	0
TOTAL LIABILITIES:	**65.00**

NET WORTH (total assets minus total liabilities):	**785.00**

Your Financial Statement

ASSETS (what you own)   **Date** _____

     Cash and checking account _____

     Savings _____

     Stocks and bonds _____

     Coins _____

     Car _____

     Furniture/Electronics _____

     Jewelry _____

     Other personal items _____

     Other assets _____

TOTAL ASSETS: _____

LIABILITIES (what you owe)

     Current bills _____

     Credit card debt _____

     Car loan _____

     Personal debts to relatives _____

     Educational loans _____

     Bank loans _____

     Other debts _____

TOTAL LIABILITIES: _____

NET WORTH (total assets minus total liabilities): _____

Prayer Logs

Prayer Logs

"Pray for one another" (JAMES 5:16).

Name_____   Parents _____

Home phone_____   Brothers and Sisters _____

Cell phone _____   _____

E-mail _____   _____

Home address _____   _____

_____   _____

WEEK	PRAYER REQUEST(S)	ANSWERS TO PRAYER
1		
2		
3		
4		
5		
6		
7		
8		
9		
10	My long-term prayer request:	

"Pray for one another" (JAMES 5:16).

Name _____ Parents _____

Home phone _____ Brothers and Sisters _____

Cell phone _____ _____

E-mail _____ _____

Home address _____ _____

_____ _____

Week	PRAYER REQUEST(S)	ANSWERS TO PRAYER
1		
2		
3		
4		
5		
6		
7		
8		
9		
10	My long-term prayer request:	

"Pray for one another" (JAMES 5:16).

Name _____ Parents _____

Home phone _____ Brothers and Sisters _____

Cell phone _____ _____

E-mail _____ _____

Home address _____ _____

_____ _____

WEEK	PRAYER REQUEST(S)	ANSWERS TO PRAYER
1		
2		
3		
4		
5		
6		
7		
8		
9		
10	My long-term prayer request:	

"Pray for one another" (JAMES 5:16).

Name _____   Parents _____

Home phone _____   Brothers and Sisters _____

Cell phone _____   _____

E-mail _____   _____

Home address _____   _____

_____   _____

WEEK	PRAYER REQUEST(S)	ANSWERS TO PRAYER
1		
2		
3		
4		
5		
6		
7		
8		
9		
10	My long-term prayer request:	

"Pray for one another" (JAMES 5:16).

Name_____   Parents _____

Home phone_____   Brothers and Sisters _____

Cell phone _____   _____

E-mail _____   _____

Home address _____   _____

_____   _____

WEEK	PRAYER REQUEST(S)	ANSWERS TO PRAYER
1		
2		
3		
4		
5		
6		
7		
8		
9		
10	My long-term prayer request:	

"Pray for one another" (JAMES 5:16).

Name_____   Parents _____

Home phone_____   Brothers and Sisters _____

Cell phone _____   _____

E-mail _____   _____

Home address _____   _____

_____   _____

Week	Prayer Request(s)	Answers to Prayer
1		
2		
3		
4		
5		
6		
7		
8		
9		
10	My long-term prayer request:	

"Pray for one another" (JAMES 5:16).

Name_____ Parents _____

Home phone_____ Brothers and Sisters _____

Cell phone _____ _____

E-mail _____ _____

Home address _____ _____

_____ _____

WEEK	PRAYER REQUEST(S)	ANSWERS TO PRAYER
1		
2		
3		
4		
5		
6		
7		
8		
9		
10	My long-term prayer request:	